Corrections

New Identification

No 64: This is most likely Charles Taylor as Farmer Gammon in John O'Keeffe's play *Wild Oats: or, The Strolling Gentleman* – which was revived at Drury Lane Theatre on 14 November 1829 with a Mr Tayleure [sic] in the part.

Nos 78 and 79: Unidentified actor as Marrall in *A New Way to Pay Old Debts* by Philip Massinger. By an unknown artist signed "D. Wilde" Mid 1820s. Two pencil and wash sketches (36.7 cms x 23.2 cms) (14¾" x 9¼"). These two sketches on paper water-marked 1825, would appear to be from a sketchbook (other roughs are on the reverse). They are of the same actor in the same costume and, though having a contemporary inscription and a signature 'D. Wilde', are obviously not by Samuel De Wilde.

The pencil inscriptions are:

No 78: Mar. Hang up Jack Marrall
Scene 2nd Act 4th.

No 79: Marrall: I! No, I assure you:
           I have a conscience etc.
           Act 5th Scene 1.

These lines come from two speeches of Marrall – 'A Creature of Sir Giles Overreach' – in Massinger's play, written in 1633. It provided a great vehicle for Edmund Kean as Sir Giles Overreach from 1816. He was painted in a scene from the play by Clint in 1820 (now in the Garrick Club). In this painting, Joseph Munden is playing Marrall.

Kean was playing in *A New Way to Pay Old Debts* at Drury Lane during 1825 (performances are recorded on 31 January and 22 June). Marrall was on both occasions played by Daniel Terry (see No 58). It is suggested that these two sketches may be associated with these performances.

Guide to the Maugham Collection of Theatrical Paintings

by **Raymond Mander and Joe Mitchenson**

Guide to the
Maugham Collection of
Theatrical Paintings
is an NT paperback

Published by Heinemann and the National Theatre
Financed by the Trustee of the
Shakespeare Memorial National Theatre Trust

ISBN 43 518 591 8

Editor of this Guide Iain Mackintosh
General Editor of the NT paperback series John Goodwin
Editorial Assistant Lyn Haill

Printed by Battley Brothers, Clapham, London SW4 0JN
and designed by Ted Sawtell
Photoset in Plantin

Introduction by W Somerset Maugham
reprinted by kind permission of
William Heinemann Ltd and the Estate of
W Somerset Maugham. Remainder of text
© National Theatre of Great Britain 1980

National Theatre
South Bank
London SE1 9PX

Contents

Catalogue and Exhibition Notes
The Collection has been numbered chronologically **1** to **83** by the span of each artist's work – e.g. Zoffany or copies of Zoffany (**3** to **10**) in date order of being painted after the Hayman (**2**) and before the copies of Reynolds and of Dance (**11** and **12**). The first section ends with Stothard (**20**) and the second section starts with the largest group in the Collection, oils and watercolours by De Wilde (**21** to **64**).

Dimensions are given in centimetres followed by the equivalent in inches set in brackets.

So that the Guide may be read as a book there is, facing each description, a black and white reproduction of the picture described, whether or not it is also reproduced in colour in one of the two colour sections.

The Collection is on permanent exhibition in the NT foyers. The hanging has been arranged by Geoffrey Ashton (Librarian, the Garrick Club) and Iain Mackintosh.

Guide to the Maugham Collection of Theatrical Paintings

Preface

by Raymond Mander and Joe Mitchenson

Until now the fortunes of the Maugham collection of theatrical paintings have been precarious to say the least. Indeed its survival in its entirety is little short of a miracle. It was housed at Maugham's home, the Villa Mauresque in the south of France, but at the Occupation he was forced to leave the country. His paintings, amongst other personal belongings, were stored and cared for by a kindly neighbour. On Maugham's return home in 1946, he found that his villa had been occupied by both the Germans and the Italians, but his collection was safe and sound. It was rehung in the villa, until first the oils and later the watercolours came to London.

In November 1948 it was announced that Somerset Maugham was bequeathing his collection of over forty oil paintings and a similar number of watercolours to the Trustees of the National Theatre – to decorate the theatre when the building should be finally realised. In 1951 he handed over all the oil paintings to the Trustees, who arranged for their exhibition at the Victoria and Albert Museum.

It was at the Private View on 18 July that we first saw the collection. Of the pictures exhibited, ten were said to be of unknown actors or subjects, six were incorrectly identified, titled, or attributed. We note this to explain why, in several of the consequent press reports and articles on the exhibition and the collection, wrong titles were given; and there is reference to pictures which would appear not to exist in the collection.

It must be offered in excuse for this, that the V & A received with the pictures a numbered schedule, with no corresponding numbers on the pictures, and this schedule had numerous errors (which appear to have come through a manuscript list being wrongly typed); and also that the dubious titling of some of the pictures had been of many years' standing. It was a desire to arrive at a better knowledge of the pictures that caused us, at the request of Kenneth Rae on behalf of the Trustees, to start work on a catalogue.

This labour of love was published four years later in 1955 by William Heinemann as *The Artist and the Theatre*, when the oils were exhibited at the Times Book Shop; they then went into storage.

The watercolours did not come to London until after Maugham's death in December 1965. We first saw them later the following year and quickly listed and recorded all the information on the frames and mounts before they too joined the oils in store. Like these, they were accompanied by a very misleading schedule. Some of the watercolours were later shown at *The De Wildes*, an exhibition organised by Ian Mayes at Northampton in 1971, and also a selection of watercolours and oils was lent to *The Georgian Playhouse 1730-1830*, an Arts Council Exhibition devised by Iain Mackintosh and Geoffrey Ashton and held in 1975 at the Hayward Gallery in celebration of the opening of the National Theatre.

The oils and watercolours have now been thoroughly cleaned and restored for final exhibition, as originally planned.

The present guide adds to our original work to include the water-colours, thereby covering the entire Maugham collection. We hope that this new publication will bring to the reader the excitement of discovery and identification which we ourselves experienced.

We do not pretend to be art experts – our interest has been in the subjects of the paintings. Naturally the art side has entered into our researches, but comment on the respective merits of the paintings must rest with the expert. We have tried to bring the pictures to life, to show the background of the actors and the plays depicted.

To credit everyone whom we have consulted or who has helped us over the past twenty-eight years would fill this book. A list in *The Artist and the Theatre* covers the notes on the oil paintings. But for this final guide we would like to add our special thanks to our editor

Iain Mackintosh, and to Sir Ralph Richardson and Denys Sutton for their valued contributions. Similarly we offer our thanks to Betty Beesley and Pamela Lumsden of the Garrick Club Archives, and Stanley Gillam of the London Library, who made rare texts available; the Theatre Museum, particularly Jennifer Aylmer who has taken endless pains to answer queries and trace performances, as did Anthony Latham whilst a member of their staff. Geoffrey Ashton has been most helpful, in particular with the biographies of the artists, as has Elizabeth Einberg of the Tate Gallery. Ian Mayes has, with his knowledge of De Wilde, taken great interest in this section, and has been of great assistance.

As so often, we have to thank Colin Mabberley, the Curator of our Trust, who has worked with us throughout the final stages of this guide, and Mary Quinnell for coping with our manuscript, the index and proofs.

Lastly, we are extremely grateful for the encouragement of John Goodwin and Lyn Haill at the National Theatre, without whose confidence the work would never have been attempted or completed.

We hope that interest and new scholarship will be revived by the housing and display of the complete collection as envisaged by Maugham, and the publication by the National Theatre of this guide.

Introduction

by W Somerset Maugham

I began collecting theatrical pictures two or three years before the First World War. It was pure accident. I was at that time a popular author of light comedies, and on the strength of the money they brought me, I bought the lease of a small house in Chesterfield Street. It was built in 1734 and so the lease had over eight hundred years to run. One day Hugh Lane dropped in to see me and told me that he had seen in a shop in Pimlico a theatrical picture by De Wilde which he thought uncommonly good.

'They're only asking forty-five pounds for it,' he said, 'you're a dramatist, you ought to buy it.'

I went to see it. It represented two actors in a scene from *Sylvester Daggerwood*. I liked it and bought it. Not very long afterwards, in April 1914, there was a sale at Christie's which included a theatrical picture that had belonged to Henry Irving, and because I had one I bought another. It was Zoffany's portrait of Garrick and Mrs Cibber in Otway's *Venice Preserv'd*, and I paid twenty-nine pounds for it; then I acquired a smaller version said to be by Benjamin West of Reynolds's huge picture of *Garrick Between Tragedy and Comedy*, which is now in the possession of Lord Rothschild. I forget what it cost me, but certainly very little, for at that time nobody was much interested in such pictures. After that it was all up to me. I began to frequent sales, and whenever a theatrical picture came up which I liked I bid for it and generally got it. Foster's auction room in King Street soon became a rewarding hunting-ground. Every week the walls would be thickly covered with pictures of all sorts, mostly very indifferent; and now and again I came across a single figure of an actor in costume, grimy and badly wanting restoration, but still in its original frame. I was often the only bidder, and the discouraged auctioneer knocked it down to me for a guinea or thirty shillings.

Sometimes, of course, I was unlucky. Once I saw at Christie's a Zoffany which represented Garrick as Macbeth and Mrs Pritchard as his lady, and I set my heart on having it. The bidding started slowly, and I was confident of getting it as usual for a few pounds; but to my surprise I found that a dealer I knew slightly was persistently bidding against me. We bid the picture up to a hundred pounds, to two hundred, to two hundred and fifty, which was more than had ever been paid before for one of Zoffany's theatrical pictures, and then the dealer sent me the message that he was buying the picture for the Maharajah of Baroda and his instructions were to get it at any price. I gave in and it was knocked down for two hundred and sixty pounds. But I did not only frequent auction

rooms. I haunted the junk shops, the frame makers, in Soho and Chelsea, and occasionally allowed the owners to sell me for a song a De Wilde, a Hamilton or a Smirke that they had been trying to get rid of for years.

In course of time the dealers came to know that I was a collector, and whenever they came across a theatrical picture they let me know. Naturally the price went up and I could no longer buy a picture for a pound or two. I think I was still the only collector, but a casual buyer often purchased one of these pictures that he had seen at a dealer's, who had it cleaned and varnished, because it was pleasing. These casual buyers purchased the portrait of an actress in costume not because it represented her in a famous part, but because it was a picture of an attractive woman in a pretty dress. (That is why in my collection the single figures are all of men). They paid fancy prices. It was only by chance then that I got a bargain. One of the last De Wildes I bought cost me six hundred pounds. Three or four years ago a Zoffany was sold for eight hundred and fifty pounds and shortly afterwards the dealer who bought it offered it to me for two thousand. It was a satisfaction to me to be able to tell him that I already had another version of the picture and had paid two hundred pounds for it.

This may require some explanation. The artists who specialised in this form of art often painted a replica or two of the same picture. The first one I ever bought, John Bannister and Richard Suett in *Sylvester Daggerwood*, is a replica of one at the Garrick Club; and there are four of Zoffany's *Venice Preserv'd*. Mine is considered to be the original. I don't know how one can account for this except by supposing that when two celebrated actors were painted together each wanted a copy; and it may be that now and then an admirer ordered still another copy for himself.

Theatrical pictures are a variety of genre painting, which, as we know, became popular in the Netherlands in the first half of the seventeenth century; and it is perhaps suggestive that De Wilde, the most prolific of these painters, was himself a Dutchman. Zoffany painted portraits and conversation pieces, and theatrical portraits only as a side line; but De Wilde, so far as I know, painted very little else. Artists before them had painted scenes from plays, and there is in the Louvre a drawing by Glaude Gillet, which represents such a scene; but before Zoffany only a few artists like Hogarth, Hayman and Wilson had experimented in painting actual portraits of actors in character. I doubt whether anyone can now tell whether the idea of doing this was owing to the pardonable vanity

4

Opposite: Maugham at the Villa Mauresque, 1948

of the actors, who wanted their ephemeral fame to be thus perpetuated, or whether the idea was an artist's. Anyway, it was Zoffany who started the real vogue that quickly spread. George III who, according to Hazlitt, was fond of low comedy, commissioned him to paint a scene from Frederick Reynolds's *Speculation* in which Quick, Munden and Lewis were introduced.

I have mentioned only a few of the artists who practised this modest form of art; but there were a good many others, of less talent, who took advantage of the prevailing fashion to earn a few honest guineas. The Garrick Club has a great number, I had over forty, and there must be many more scattered here and there in private houses. And it was not only oil paintings that were produced to satisfy the public demand; De Wilde, evidently to suit patrons of small means, produced in quantity single figures of actors and actresses in water colour. They are full of charm. The Garrick Club has so many that it has been able to paper the walls of a staircase with them. I had twenty-eight myself.

One may ask oneself why this vogue should have been so great as to occasion so enormous a production. I can only suggest as an answer that during the period in which these pictures were painted, the English took a passionate interest in the theatre. The public was small and there was a constant change of bill. The repertoire seems to have consisted for the most part of Shakespeare, stock plays and farces. Audiences knew the classical plays well, and the farces were seldom of merit; so it was natural enough that they should take more interest in the players than the play. Hazlitt would not have troubled to write now and then a careful analysis of a popular actor's performance in a well-known play if he had not been assured that the subject was of concern to his readers. It is likely enough that this passion for the stage should have made patrons who could afford it wish to have a picture of a favourite actor in a part that he had made his own (there are many portraits of Garrick as Richard III), and for the less affluent there were the watercolours that could be bought for a few shillings apiece. The vogue died, I surmise, when photography gave the public an even cheaper way of gratifying a very human desire. In my youth there was still a brisk sale for such photographs, and my own chimney-piece was adorned with one of the lovely Jane Hading and one of the incomparable Eleonora Duse. Now that the fan can cut pictures of the stars of the moment from the illustrated papers the demand has ceased. The pin-up girl of today is the last bastard descendant of the theatrical pictures of Zoffany and De Wilde.

My collection was second only to that of the Garrick Club, and I had spent so many years making it that I was grieved to think that it would be dispersed at my death in Christie's auction rooms. Such a collection can never be made again. Now, it had always seemed to me a shocking thing that so great a capital as London should not have a national theatre such as there is in Paris, Vienna and Berlin.

Such an institution would be a worthy monument to British drama and would give an opportunity to the foreigners who visit our country to discover that it has produced not only one dramatist of genius but many of no small merit. It might serve also to create a school of dramatists and a school of actors good enough to revive interest, now sadly diminished, in the spoken drama. When at last the long efforts of a number of enthusiastic persons, striving indefatigably year after year to overcome the indifference of governments and the apathy of the public, seemed likely to be crowned with success and a national theatre would be built, it struck me that by presenting my pictures to it I might achieve my object of keeping them together. Theatres in the eighteenth century with their rococo decorations, with the red curtains to the boxes, with their immense chandeliers, had a glamour which put you in a comfortable state of mind to enjoy the play you were about to witness. The theatres they build now are severely functional; you can see from all parts of them what is happening on the stage; the seats are comfortable and there are abundant exits, so that you run small chance of being burnt to death. But they are cold. They are apt to make you feel that you have come to the playhouse to undergo an ordeal rather than to enjoy an entertainment. It seemed to me that my pictures in the foyer and on the stairs of a new theatre would a trifle mitigate the austerity of the architect's design. I offered them to the Trustees of the National Theatre and they were good enough to accept them.

This handsome volume, to which these words I have written are meant to serve as an introduction, owes its origin to the enthusiasm and formidable industry of two young men, Raymond Mander and Joe Mitchenson. They have put an immense amount of work into it. They have pored over dusty volumes, searched collections, examined innumerable faded playbills, read old criticisms of plays and looked into the records of sales at auction rooms. They have spared no pains to make their information accurate. They have followed clues with all the pertinacity of a detective of fiction; and so have been able to identify an obscure actor in a forgotten play, and in some cases have even been able to quote the very words he was saying at the moment the artist chose to picture the scene. They have corrected mistakes in attribution; they have been able to decide which was the original painting and which the replica. They are true lovers of the theatre, and their labour has been a labour of love. I like to think that it will not have been entirely wasted, for what they have learnt is surely not without interest, since these pictures, which have been so admirably photographed, will eventually find their permanent place in the National Theatre and there, I trust, give pleasure to generation after generation of playgoers.

Cap Ferrat 1954

Reprinted from *The Artist and the Theatre* by Raymond Mander and Joe Mitchenson, published Heinemann 1955

Art and the Theatre

by Denys Sutton

The theatre has attracted artists over the centuries. They have worked for it by designing sets and costumes and they have represented performers and performances. The interplay of gestures and the varieties of facial expression seen on stage have appealed to artists such as Watteau and Degas; some have been fascinated by the glint of light on gilded boxes or the appearance of the members of the audience.

The extent to which Baroque painting was influenced by the contemporary stage – Bernini was a man of the theatre – is never sufficiently stressed. Would Bolognese or Roman painting be quite the same without theatrical inspiration? Moreover, stage illusionism is inherent in baroque and rococo wall decoration.

Contact with the theatre has some influence on the artist's colours (those of Degas, for instance) and on his general way of painting, as may be seen with Sickert's work. The light effects found in Zoffany's painting of David Garrick and Mrs Cibber in *Venice Preserv'd* (**3**) are unusual for the period. The strong light from the candles on stage creates the sort of mysterious impression encountered in late nineteenth-century painting. The backcloth in this work may be compared to one of Whistler's nocturnes.

Whistler's own approach to painting is theatrical, and his portraits of men and women often look like actors and actresses. His painting of Henry Irving as Philip of Spain is the prototype for many of his others; his own late self-portrait (at Washington) could be that of a Victorian actor-manager.

The painter of stage performances needs to possess a particular aptitude for this exciting if exacting genre. He has to be skilled in relating one figure to another and, at the same time, in implying, however casually, the meaning of the scene. This is a type of painting that runs counter to the old theory that the formal character of a painting was all that mattered. On the contrary, the point of such work is that it does express an idea – namely that of the action of actors and actresses at a given time, in a specific play. Zoffany's achievement lay in his ability to do just this in such a cheerful canvas as that representing three actors in *Love in a Village* (**4**), which was first performed at Covent Garden Theatre in 1762.

Such painting may be considered as an extension of the conversation piece, a genre of which Zoffany was a master. His success as a painter of stage scenes lies in his gift for being able to suggest that action is taking place. When we see Garrick performing as Sir John Brute in Vanbrugh's *The Provok'd Wife* (**6**), presumably we are being shown the actor as he looked then, and that he is wearing the costume he did on stage. Zoffany's grasp of character and eye for succulent paint heighten the effect. Are such paintings realistic? No doubt only up to a point, and, in any event, they provide an image that impresses us as being true. This is also true of Toulouse Lautrec's representations of the Moulin Rouge and other night spots of the 'nineties in Paris. If these are compared with photographs of the same places, it may be seen how the artist has introduced a note of glamour.

The relationship between the romantic movement and the stage is clear: for example, Delacroix derived considerable inspiration from Shakespeare. One of the most remarkable pictures in the Maugham Collection is Zoffany's representation of Charles Macklin as Shylock (**8**), significantly the first occasion on which this character was presented sympathetically on stage. The romantic character of the sky, the intensity of Macklin's face and his stance – these not only bring out this actor's interpretation of the part, but also anticipate by some forty years the approach associated with the Romantics.

Zoffany painted much else besides the theatre. This was not so with Samuel De Wilde, an artist of Dutch extraction and thus a compatriot of Cornelis Troost. De Wilde was stage-struck, and his paintings and his remarkably fresh watercolours (**36** to **64**) present a vivid panorama of the golden age of English acting. His gift for capturing the mood created by an actor is shown in his vivid picture of Thomas Collins as Slender in *The Merry Wives of Windsor* and Charles Farley as Francisco in *A Tale of Mystery* in which the Gothic character of the play is faithfully reflected in the stage setting and furniture. His watercolours show many of the great actors, such as Macready, in character and the depiction of him in *Richard III* is brilliant (**57**).

For the reconstruction of both the staging of plays and the performances of actors paintings often provide the best possible evidence, and when these are done by an artist of quality the result is all the more exciting.

On Looking at Gifts

by Ralph Richardson

A few of us, a million or so perhaps, are happy that they have been given a present, a gift; they have been given a National Theatre; it is a present from the rest of the congregation – God bless them for it and we thank them. We few value the theatre and feel that it is a fine instrument to express the poetry of which nationally we possess a rich store.

There is a delicate charm connected with gifts. "What a gifted child" is a magic thing to hear said. There are emotions in accepting gifts from other people; there are laws, and indeed there are sins concerning them – it is forbidden to look a gift horse in the mouth.

Now we have been given a theatre. We have also been given a house-warming present to put in it. We may look at this gift, it is not a horse; it is a collection of pictures, and the donor is the late Somerset Maugham.

It is not unlikely that Somerset Maugham was born in modern dress; his birthday suit of the best stuff, elegantly cut. His novels and short stories come off the page as light and as easy as ever; and when his play *For Services Rendered*, written in the early 1930s, was put on at the National Theatre it sprang out of the band-box without a crease.

Now the National Theatre has received from "Willie" Maugham, as his friends called him, this house-warming gift, and in these pages there is an article written by him, in itself a perfect example of his graceful style, as he explains where and how he found these gifts, and of his intention to bequeath them to this theatre.

The pictures are valuable and for the author's admirers they are the more interesting in that they reflect something of the giver.

These portraits painted long ago are remarkably vivid and alive. The subjects stand completely at ease; though in velvet with silver buttons they are modern and might give a tip for tomorrow's race at Brighton.

Now Willie's wish and will has brought these pictures to us and one hopes they will warm and decorate the house. Perhaps Maugham might not object if one or two of these old strollers were allowed to go back-stage. One of them might hang in Peter Hall's office. He, unlike many directors, actually likes actors. There are already photographs of several on his wall. Another picture might go to an actor's dressing room. What a hint with a wink the artful old craftsman might give to the modern actor.

The British Theatre at the end of the Eighteenth Century: a Golden Age?

by Iain Mackintosh

The Maugham collection of theatrical paintings spans a period of eighty-seven years, from 1759 (**2**, Garrick as Richard III) to 1846 (**77**, Davidge as Malvolio). Three-quarters of these date from between 1790 and 1830, a period in which no great play was written but for which two claims can certainly be made that this was a Golden Age.

First, theatre in Britain was popular in a way that it never had been before and never has been since. In 1771 Sir Robert Talbot wrote in *The Oxford Magazine:* 'As it was in Athens the playhouse in London is for all classes of the nation. The peer of the realm, the gentleman, the merchant, the citizen, the clergyman, the tradesman and their wives, resort thither to take places and the crowd is great.' Nor was it only in London, as in the reigns of Queen Elizabeth and of King James, that the theatre so occupied the minds of men. While in 1714 there had been only one regular theatre in all Britain, a hundred years later James Winston, researching in the first decade of the nineteenth century for his *Theatre Tourist*, was able to note over 300 theatres outside of London.

In the middle of the century David Garrick, actor manager of Drury Lane from 1747 to 1776, had enlisted the help of the fine artist in placing theatre at the centre of society. Major artists of the day, including Hayman, Zoffany and Reynolds (**2** to **11**), had recorded in oils his great performances. From these paintings engravings were made and printed in great numbers to satisfy the hundreds of theatre enthusiasts across the country. These might have to make do with an engraving or a journey to London because Garrick, once established, never toured. But in the next generations the drama and the players radiated throughout Britain and beyond to America and Europe until, in 1828, it could be recorded that W C Macready, the Eminent Tragedian (**57**), visited twenty-three towns and cities in Britain outside London, plus Drury Lane and Paris twice, in a single year.

In the 1830s and 1840s, the theatre slumped alarmingly. The reasons are many and must include the aftermath of war, the rise of sectarianism, economic recession (coupled ironically with the growth of the railway system) and, most significantly, divisions within society which resulted in the upper classes withdrawing their support from the playhouses while much of the working classes was no longer able to afford the high prices of admission. (When the next theatre boom came toward the end of the nineteenth century no longer would a single theatre attract all classes; rather would each strata of society stay with its own branch of entertainment in different sorts of theatre, ranging from Italian Opera to Penny Gaff). By 1840 the managers both of the metropolitan patent theatres, Drury Lane and Covent Garden, and of the provincial circuit theatres were trying everything to recover lost popularity. Vulgar spectacle was substituted for theatre magic. In place of great tragedy came melodrama that externalised the emotions, reducing dramatic conflict to black and white. In place of the old companies with their broadly based repertoire of 40 to 50 plays, ballad operas and farces, there were scratch companies supplemented with London stars or fairground novelties. 'Henceforward', mourned one commentator, 'theatres for spectators rather than playhouses for hearers.' The audiences stayed away, the art of acting declined and the victory of pageant over player signalled the end of a Golden Age.

The second claim that the period up to 1830 was a Golden Age rests on the fact that the Georgian theatre was an actors' theatre. Unlike every other country in Europe there was no princely patron to pay the bills. In 1747 Dr Johnson had written: 'The Drama's laws the Drama's patrons give'. Princely patrons may prefer French dancers and Italian singers: in Georgian Britain the public voice demanded actors acting and in a repertoire that showed all its favourites to best advantage. Here the Maugham pictures are invaluable because they provide a wide view of the acting profession. In the set-piece oils the actor managers and their leading players are recorded for their own pleasure or that of a wealthy enthusiast, while in the twenty-eight watercolours by De Wilde (**36** to **63**) can be seen many of the smaller part players who would visit his studio, conveniently set between Drury Lane and Covent Garden, to have their individual theatrical achievements set down for posterity. The plays, too, represent the spectrum of entertainment, from the classic tragedies of Shakespeare and of Otway to the lighter weight sentimental comedies. These pictures also remind us that most productions until the turn of the century were in modern dress, that is in a style of dress identical to that of the audience.

To be present at the four or five hour programme presented nightly at a Georgian playhouse (mainpiece, afterpiece and often entractes or a curtain raiser) was an experience closer to that of attending Shakespeare's Globe than seeing a show at either an Edwardian West End theatre or today's National Theatre. Into the pit and encircling boxes and gallery were crammed three times as many people as are permitted to occupy the same space today – what must it have felt to be one of these actors and set such a house in a roar! The actor could see the audience and each member of the audience could see most of his or her fellows because the lights in the auditorium could not be dimmed until the widespread introduction of gas lighting controls in the second half of the nineteenth century. The theatres were generally small in size, no larger than the Theatre Royal Bristol (1766) or perhaps the Old Vic of Waterloo Road (1818 and 1871), save that is for the new Drury Lane and Covent Garden which were rebuilt at twice the size of their predecessors in 1794 and 1792. But while these latter two elephantine theatres were the first to be given over to 'the splendour of the scenes, the ingenuity of the machinist and the rich display of dresses aided by the captivating charms of music', in the minor London theatres and in the country playhouses the players stood firm for another generation.

These players stood and played on the bare boards of the Georgian forestage with audience all around save in the narrow proscenium with its scenic stage beyond. They had little but their talent as actors with which to 'on your imaginary forces work'. Today you may need to make your own leap of the imagination to conjure up the context of pit, box and gallery papered with people. But there is no doubt that these remarkable Maugham paintings will people that world with a whole company of players from what these pictures show so decisively to have been a Golden Age.

8 Zoffany Charles Macklin in *The Merchant of Venice*
see page *18*

3 Zoffany David Garrick and Susannah Maria Cibber in *Venice Preserv'd*
see page *14*

13 Hamilton Sarah Siddons in *Cleone*
see page *20*

4 Zoffany Edward Shuter, John Beard and John Dunstall in *Love in a Village*
see page *14*

15 Smirke scene from *Love for Love*
see page *20*

11 after **Reynolds** David Garrick between the Muses of Tragedy and Comedy
see page *18*

Catalogue

David Garrick? (1717-1779)
by Jean-Baptiste van Loo?
oil   89.5 × 70 (35½ × 27½)

1

This painting came into the collection in 1947 with the attribution: David Garrick by Van Loo c 1742. Its previous history is unknown. When *The Artist and the Theatre* was published in 1954 a case supporting this attribution was put forward.

The picture would appear to have been painted during Van Loo's stay in London from 1737 to 1742, probably in 1740-41 when Garrick was 23 or 24. He first appeared on the stage in London in October 1741 at Goodman's Fields, and at Drury Lane in 1742. His play *Lethe* had been produced at Drury Lane in 1740, and he acted in his own farce *The Lying Valet* in 1741. He quickly became the most popular actor of his day, and according to contemporary accounts dressed well.

The literary side of his career is stressed by the books and writing material in the picture, and he is shown in very elaborate and fashionable clothes.

Support is given by comparison with other engraved portraits of Garrick after he had achieved fame as an actor, notably the earliest engraving dated 1745 after a portrait by Arthur Pond. Another version of this is titled: 'David Garrick (Gentleman), one of His Majesty's Servants, as he appeared (aged 25) in London'. This would suggest that the Pond portrait was painted at the time of his first appearance at Drury Lane in 1742. The resemblance of the sitter to the Van Loo portrait is striking. The latter would then be the earliest of the portraits of Garrick now in existence, as it seems to be of Garrick the dramatist and poet (1740) rather than Garrick the famous actor (October 1741).

Another field of speculation is opened up by comparing the picture with a portrait of Peg Woffington, also attributed to Van Loo and now in the Hanbury Williams family collection. Peg Woffington first appeared in London in 1740. Her association with Garrick on the stage started in May 1742, when he first appeared at Drury Lane as King Lear to her Cordelia. He is known to have long admired her, and from that time also dates their off-stage relationship. In June they left London together for a summer season in Dublin. Some writers, however, insist that they were lovers from 1740-41, before Garrick himself went on the stage. The similar size (known as kit-cat) of the two portraits suggest that they may have been a pair, painted at that time by the same artist.

When the painting of Garrick was exhibited at the Hayward Gallery Exhibition, *The Georgian Playhouse 1730-1830,* doubts were expressed concerning the attributions, but no alternative suggestion was forthcoming, so it remains in this guide with a question mark hanging over it.

2 David Garrick (1717-1779) as Gloucester
Richard III by William Shakespeare
Drury Lane 1759
by **Francis Hayman**
oil   89.5 × 64 (35¼ × 25¼)

David Garrick is depicted in the Bosworth Field scene (Act V Scene 8 in the Colley Cibber version, in use at the time), at the line:

"A horse, a horse! My kingdom for a horse."

The part of Gloucester was closely associated with Garrick throughout his career. He made his formal London debut in the part at the Goodman's Field Theatre on 19 October 1741. His appearance was a sensation and he was engaged for Drury Lane, where he first appeared on 11 May 1742. He became manager of the theatre in 1747 and remained actor-manager until he retired from the stage in 1776.

Richard III was often revived, and it was Garrick who introduced the innovation of 'period' costume, though the other characters continued to be dressed in what was then contemporary attire. He was painted in the part by Hogarth (1746), Hayman (1760) and Dance (1771). The play was performed at Drury Lane on 8 March 1759, by command of His Royal Highness the Prince of Wales, and it is most likely that Hayman began this picture then as Garrick did not play the part again until 22 May 1760, by which time the painting, signed with the initials 'F.H.' and dated 1760, had been shown by the artist at the Society of Artists Exhibition of that year. It was engraved by William Bromley in 1811.

3 David Garrick (1717-1779) as Jaffier
Susannah Maria Cibber (1714-1776) as Belvidera
Venice Preserv'd, or A Plot Discovered by Thomas Otway
Drury Lane Theatre 1762-3
by **Johan Zoffany**
oil   101.5 × 127 (40 × 50)

Venice Preserv'd, or A Plot Discovered is the most famous play of Thomas Otway (1652-1685). It was first produced at the Duke's Theatre, Dorset Garden on 7 February 1682, with William Smith as Jaffier, Thomas Betterton as Pierre, and Elizabeth Barry as Belvidera.

After Otway left Oxford he hoped to become an actor, but only made one successful appearance in 1670. He then turned to playwriting, and in 1675 his first play *Alcibiades* was produced. He followed this with a number of works, of which *The Orphan* and *Venice Preserv'd* rank among the finest of their period. These two plays held the stage for over a hundred and fifty years.

The story concerns a plot by Pierre and a band of conspirators to overthrow the Venetian republic. His friend, Jaffier (married to Belvidera, a senator's daughter) is persuaded to join in. Belvidera persuades her husband to save her father by exposing the plot, which he does, on the Senate's promise that all would be pardoned. Pierre knows Jaffier has betrayed him, and when the Senate retract their promise, Pierre is condemned to death. Jaffier, in despair, threatens to kill Belvidera and himself but relents. This is the moment in Act IV Scene 2 depicted in the painting:

Belvidera: "What wilt thou do? Ah, do not kill me, Jaffier."

Jaffier goes to see his friend, and, on the scaffold, kills Pierre rather than he should suffer a traitor's death. He then takes his own life. The news is brought to Belvidera who already half distracted, dies when she hears of the double tragedy.

Zoffany's painting of Garrick and Mrs Cibber in this play, was exhibited at the Society of Artists in 1763. The play was revived in the 1762/63 season on 20 October 1762, so it is most likely that the picture was painted at that time.

Jaffier in the painting is shown in contemporary clothes. Belvidera

wears a black satin dress decorated with white lace. In the background is a distant view of San Giorgio Maggiore.

There are at least four versions of this picture: the Maugham is thought to be the version engraved by McArdell in 1764. It once belonged to Sir Henry Irving. The others are in the collections of Lord Lambton, the Garrick Club, and the Budapest Museum of Fine Arts. The main difference in the versions seems to lie in the different designs of the material of Garrick's waistcoat.

4 Edward Shuter (1728-1776) as Justice Woodcock
John Beard (1716-1791) as Hawthorn
John Dunstall (1717-1778) as Hodge
Love in a Village by Isaac Bickerstaffe
Covent Garden Theatre 1762
by **Johan Zoffany**
oil   101.5 × 127 (40 × 50)

The painting is of Act I Scene 2 with the cast of the original production (8 December 1762). The scene is the Hall in Justice Woodcock's House, when Hodge, Woodcock's servant, has just entered with the news of the Statute Fair, for the hiring of servants, to be held that day on the village green. Woodcock grumbles about it and says he will have it stopped another year. His neighbour defends the Fair, and says he himself intends to go to it.

Woodcock: "I wish, Master Hawthorn, that I could teach you to be a little more sedate: why won't you take pattern by me, and consider your dignity? Odd's heart, I don't wonder you are not a rich man; you laugh too much ever to be rich."

Hawthorn: "Right! Neighbour Woodcock! Health, good humour, and competence, is my motto: and, if my executors have a mind, they are welcome to make it my epitaph."

Love in a Village, a ballad opera, was derived from several older sources. The music consisted chiefly of old airs arranged by Dr Thomas Arne, with one or two famous opera tunes, six songs entirely new, and an original overture by Karl Abel. Isaac Bickerstaffe (1735-1812) was considered by his contemporaries to be the equal of John Gay in the field of ballad opera. He wrote some twenty plays and operas, among the most successful of which were *The Maid of the Mill, Lionel and Clarissa* and *The Padlock*. In 1772, he was forced to leave the country to avoid facing a capital charge – a scandal in which scurrilous attempts were made at the time to implicate David Garrick. In 1782 he was said to be still living abroad 'to which *a deed without a name* has banished him, and where he exists, poor and despised by all orders of people'. He died in France, forgotten but for his work, in 1812.

Zoffany exhibited a painting of *Love in a Village* in 1767 and again in the following year, both at the Society of Artists. These may be one and the same painting, but two versions of the picture exist. It is likely that the second version is the one now in the Maugham collection, and the first version, which was engraved by John Finlayson in 1768, is the one now in Detroit. In this picture the painting on the wall behind the actors is of *The Judgement of Solomon*, and in the second version, it is changed to *The Children of Charles I*, a Van Dyck now in the Royal Collection.

3 in colour on page *10*

2

4 in colour on page *11*

5 **Edward Shuter** (1728-1776) as Justice Woodcock
John Beard (1716-1791) as Hawthorn
John Dunstall (1717-1778) as Hodge
Love in a Village by Isaac Bickerstaffe
Covent Garden Theatre 1762
after **Johan Zoffany** by John Finlayson?
oil   39 × 53 (15½ × 21)

This picture (and **9**) are painted in a manner technically known as *en grisaille*. This uses tones of black and grey: the result is very much like an engraving. It was a method sometimes used by engravers for their copy of the original picture from which to make their plate. For various reasons it was not always possible for the engraver to have the original picture in his studio: sometimes it was too large – and sometimes the purchaser at the exhibition wanted the picture immediately after it had been shown. Often when a painting was engraved some years after its execution the original could not be transported to the engraver's studio. In these cases the engraver himself (who was often a competent artist in other media) or another artist would be employed to make a copy of the painting *in situ*, from which the engraver then worked.

It is interesting that the picture on the back wall, which Zoffany changed in the two versions of the picture (**4** and the painting now in Detroit), is left out completely in the *grisaille*. This concentrates mainly on the three figures, marking the highlights in monochrome, exactly as followed in the mezzotint, in what may be termed an engraver's shorthand. There is no other theory for the existence of these two pictures (**5** and **9**), nor is there any trace of their previous history.

6 **David Garrick** (1717-1779) as Sir John Brute
The Provok'd Wife by Sir John Vanbrugh
Drury Lane Theatre 1763
by **Johan Zoffany**
oil   75 × 62 (29½ × 24½)

During a drunken frolic with Lord Rake and Colonel Bully, Brute intercepts a tailor in Covent Garden taking home a new dress to his wife. He insists on putting it on, and is arrested by the Watch for making a street disturbance. This is the moment depicted in the painting:

Sir John: "Sirrah, I am Bonducca, Queen of the Welchmen; and with a leek as long as my pedigree, I will destroy your Roman legion in an instant. Britons, strike home!" (Snatches a Watchman's staff, strikes the Watch, drives them off, and returns in custody).

Taken before the Justice of the Peace, still in disguise, he gives his name as 'Lady John Brute' and is dismissed. The rest of the play concerns Lady Brute's intrigues, which in the end are forgiven by her husband, and all ends happily. This incident is different from that in the original version of the play. There Brute waylays a tailor with a clergyman's cassock which he steals and in which he appears before the magistrate. It was probably re-written as a 'drag' scene when Colley Cibber acted the part in 1716. Cibber was a notorious tinkerer with plays and most likely added it in order to satirise female fashion of the day. *The Provok'd Wife*, a comedy by Sir John Vanbrugh (1664-1726), was first produced at the Lincoln's Inn Theatre in 1697, with Thomas Betterton in the part of Brute. The play is said to have been written while Vanbrugh was in prison in Paris, during the war with France. It is not so well known now as his play *The Relapse, or Virtue in Danger,* though it was constantly played during the eighteenth century. Vanbrugh is best known as the architect of such houses as Blenheim Palace and Castle Howard; the theatre was to him a hobby early in his career. Never-theless he wrote some six successful plays and left his mark on the evoluton of English comedy. He designed the King's Theatre in the Haymarket (on the site of the present Her Majesty's Theatre) for Betterton's company in 1705.

Brute was one of David Garrick's most famous comedy roles. He first played the part at Drury Lane Theatre in 1774, and it remained a favourite throughout his career. By the cast shown with him in a full version of the picture with the Watch, it would appear to have been painted at the time of the revival of the play at Drury Lane on 18 April 1763. It is recorded in Henry Angelo's *Reminiscences* (1830) that Garrick sat for the picture at Zoffany's studio in the Piazza, Covent Garden. The solo painting is most likely a preliminary study made at this time. Garrick is said to have disliked the head, and Zoffany repainted it at his request. This may explain the oval 'repair' to the canvas, which has been cut out and replaced, on the Maugham picture which originally belonged to Garrick. The 'repair' also appears in the orginal full version now in Lord Normanby's collection.

A final version of the full picture with the alterations, which was also purchased by Garrick, remained in his family until 1972, and is now in Wolverhampton Art Gallery. It was engraved by Finlayson in 1768.

7 **David Garrick** (1717-1779) as Lord Chalkstone
Ellis Ackman (17?-1774) as Bowman
Astley Bransby (1720-1789) as Aesop
Lethe by David Garrick
Drury Lane Theatre 1766
by **Johan Zoffany**
oil   99 × 123 (39 × 48½)

The moment depicted is the scene between Aesop, the philosopher; Lord Chalkstone, a gouty old aristocrat, and Bowman, his companion.

Bowman: "Does your Lordship propose a wager as proof of the goodness of your head?"

The plot is slight – the scene is 'A Grove with a view of the river Lethe'. Mortals have been allowed to come to Elysium and drink the waters of Lethe in order to forget their miseries. In succession they arrive, escorted by Mercury, and ferried over the Styx by Charon. They are examined by Aesop, who hears their troubles and prescribes for them.

Lethe, or Aesop in the Shades was David Garrick's first essay in dramatic writing. His friendship with Charles Macklin largely influenced him in becoming an actor, but before his first appear-ance on the stage in 1741, he had begun to write plays and poetry. *Lethe*, a dramatic satire, was first produced at Drury Lane on 15 April 1740, with Henry Woodward and Kitty Clive in the cast. It remained a stock piece in Garrick's repertoire during his manage-ment of Drury Lane, and was revised on several occasions to bring its satire up to date.

Zoffany painted two scenes from *Lethe* which date from the revival in 1766 when it was performed twice: first 'by Command of Their Majesties' (George III) at Drury Lane on 23 January, a perform-ance attended also by Rousseau, the French philosopher, and second on 31 January. This dating is born out by the identification of cast on these occasions, and that the pictures were exhibited at the Society of Artists in 1766. One painting shows Garrick, Ackman and Bransby, while the other depicts Bransby (again as Aesop) with William Parsons as the Old Man and Watkins as John, his servant. Both of these are now in the Birmingham City Art Gallery. The Maugham painting is another version of the 'Garrick' scene: so far there is no known second version of the other.

5

6 in colour on cover

7

8 Charles Macklin (1700?-1797) as Shylock
The Merchant of Venice by William Shakespeare
Covent Garden 1767/68
by **Johan Zoffany**
oil   81 × 71 (32 × 28)

Shylock is depicted at the moment in Act III Scene 1 when he exclaims in the scene with Tubal: "The Curse never fell upon our Nation until now."

The date of Macklin's birth has long been in dispute, but he was probably born around 1700. He first played Shylock at Drury Lane on 14 February 1741. It was the first time, since possibly the days of Shakespeare, that Shylock had been played as a serious character and not as a figure of fun. He studied the gestures, speech and costume of the Jewish community in London and played the character as a serious study. He discarded the version of the play by Lord Lansdowne which had been in use since 1701. His experiment was a success and the performance drew from Alexander Pope the oft-quoted couplet:

> "This is the Jew
> That Shakespeare drew."

Macklin continued to play the part throughout his long career, and it was only to be expected that Zoffany would add Macklin to his fast-growing gallery of theatrical portraits. Zoffany came to England in 1758. Though performances of the play took place at Drury Lane in the season of 1759-60, Zoffany did not begin painting theatrical subjects until 1762 and it is not till 1767/68 that a series of Macklin paintings was executed. A full trial scene is now in the Tate Gallery, and there are variations and studies for the Maugham painting in other collections.

9 Samuel Foote (1720-1777) as The President (Dr Hellebore)
Thomas Weston (1737-1776) as Dr Last
The Devil Upon Two Sticks by Samuel Foote
Haymarket Theatre 1768
after **Johan Zoffany** by John Finlayson?
oil   38.5 × 63 (15¼ × 24¾)

The Devil Upon Two Sticks, a fierce satire on doctors, was written by Samuel Foote and produced at the Haymarket on 30 May 1768. The scene depicted takes place in Act III, Scene 2 in the College of Physic, where the Devil, as Dr Hellebore, hears that the rebel licentiates are marching upon them, and prepares to receive them with hosepipes from the St Dunstan's fire engine. Meanwhile Last, a cobbler and quack doctor still carrying a pair of shoes he has brought to London for a customer, is examined by the Devil and accorded his doctor's licence. The rebels arrive at the gates and are driven off with the fire-hoses. Then Last returns to fetch the shoes he had left behind. This is the moment depicted in the painting. "Well, Doctor?" asks the Devil, in the character of the President. "I have forgot my shoes," replies Last, picks them up and goes out.

Foote, a gentleman by birth, was forced by his extravagance to take up a stage career in 1744. He was not particularly successful, but his mimicry and comic abilities brought him success when he took the Little Theatre in the Haymarket in 1747 and evaded the licensing laws which allowed only the two patent theatres, Drury Lane and Covent Garden, to operate. The Little Theatre in the Haymarket had been continually in trouble for defying the larger theatres. Foote made admission by invitation to partake of tea or chocolate – which allowed the recipients to witness his entertainment. He began to write pungent satires on the topics of the day. He obtained a Royal Patent for his theatre in 1766. The original painting by Zoffany was exhibited at the Society of Artists in 1769. It is now in the collection of George Howard, and is the only version of the picture recorded. The painting in the Maugham collection is *en grisaille*, and, as with **5**, believed to have been executed by John Finlayson, who engraved his mezzotint of the picture in 1769.

10 David Garrick (1717-1779)
by an unknown artist founded on a portrait 1763
by **Johan Zoffany**
oil   74 × 61.5 (29¼ × 24¼)

This portrait, by an unknown artist painted at an unknown date, owes its origin to a portrait by Zoffany which was painted in 1763 before Garrick's continental visit (September 1763-April 1765) and had belonged to Mary Bradshaw, one of Garrick's company at Drury Lane. (Her husband was his boxkeeper.) This picture was bought by Mrs Garrick on Mrs Bradshaw's death in 1780, and left by her to her nephew in 1822, and by him to the National Gallery. It is now in the National Portrait Gallery.

For many years, the authenticity of this picture as a Zoffany was suspect, but recent cleaning has rehabilitated its origin (the original canvas is dated on the reverse "December the 31st 1763"). This painting shows Garrick without a wig and his head shaved, except for the back hair left to hold the wig in place.

Versions of the original were engraved several times with and without hair or with a wig. A portrait of Garrick by Zoffany, said to have been painted expressly for George Colman the Elder, probably between 1766 and 1769 when they were in close association, passed into the collection of Thomas Harris, the manager of Covent Garden. When sold in 1819 a note in the catalogue said: "To avoid the different changes of countenance, with which Garrick used to amuse himself while sitting for this portrait, Zoffany took this likeness concealed in an antechamber, during the times of Garrick's shaving his head, his constant custom in the afternoon." The present whereabouts of this latter picture is not known.

11 David Garrick between the Muses of Tragedy and Comedy
after **Sir Joshua Reynolds** by Mather Brown?
oil   73 × 93 (28¾ × 36¾)

Sir Joshua Reynolds painted his famous allegorical portrait of Garrick in 1760/61. It was exhibited at the Society of Artists in 1762, and is now in the collection of Lord Rothschild.

It has been said that, apart from the obvious meaning of an actor drawn from Tragedy to Comedy, the picture has a mock-heroic interpretation, inspired by the Earl of Shaftesbury's treatise on the subject of Hercules at the Crossroads, standing between Vice and Virtue. There is, in fact, a German engraving of it titled *L'Homme entre Le Vice et la vertu'*. There is also a similarity to the painting *Hercules at the Crossroads*, by Gérard de Lairesse in the Louvre.

The first engraving of the picture by E Fisher 1762 bears the title *'Reddere Personae scit convenientia cuique'* which has been rendered as

> 'That man, when need occurs, will soon invent
> For every part its proper sentiment.'

Another mezzotint has also the following title added: 'Strive not Tragedy nor Comedy to engross a Garrick who to your noblest Characters does equal honour'. The Latin line is from the *Ars Poetica* of Horace, and the English title would seem to be a very free adaptation of it.

There are at least four contemporary copies of this picture and it is possible that they may be by Mather Brown (c1763-1831), a good artist in his own right but who was also responsible for many such studio copies of Reynolds' work. The Maugham picture was at one time in the collection of Sir Henry Irving.

Horace Walpole's comment on the original painting was: "Garrick vulgar, Comedy good." It has been said that a Miss Theophila Palmer sat for the figure of Comedy. This picture has been reproduced as 'Garrick with Mrs Jordan and Mrs Siddons'; probably because the latter was painted by Reynolds as the Tragic Muse and the former by Hoppner as the Comic Muse.

8 in colour on page *9*

11 in colour on page *12*

10

12 David Garrick (1717-1779) as Gloucester
Richard III by William Shakespeare
Drury Lane 1769
after **Sir Nathaniel Dance** by an unknown artist
oil   64 × 42 (25¼ × 16½)

This is a late copy by an inferior artist of the picture by Dance which shows Garrick at the same moment in the play as does the painting by Hayman, **2**. The colours of the costume are entirely different from those in Dance's original which hangs in the Town Hall at Stratford-upon-Avon, and this copy was more than likely painted not from the original but from the 1772 mezzotint by John Dixon which is of an almost identical size.

The original painting by Dance was exhibited at the Royal Academy in 1771. It had originally been painted for Garrick himself at a stipulated price. Over dinner one evening Dance coolly told Garrick and his wife that he intended going back on his bargain as Sir Watkin Williams-Wynn had offered him a substantial increase on the price, which he had accepted. The actor received the information with well-bred aplomb, but Mrs Garrick, who had set her heart on the picture, ill concealed her vexation. She had even rearranged the pictures in the dining-room, so as to give a place of honour to the new painting. After the departure of the artist, Garrick did his best to console her with the promise that, before another day had passed, she should see the blank space filled with an even more charming picture. On the next day he led his wife to the spot, where he had had a very ornate and expensive mirror placed secretly in position, gallantly telling her that she might see the handsomer picture – in a reflection of herself.

13 Sarah Siddons (1755-1831) as Cleone
Cleone by Robert Dodsley
by **William Hamilton**
oil   49 diameter (19¼)

William Hamilton was commissioned by John Bell to execute several portraits and scenes to illustrate his *British Theatre*, which he published as separate plays between 1791 and 1797, and issued in thirty-four volumes in 1797. Each play was illustrated with a portrait of an actor or actress in a role in the play, and an engraved title page showing a scene from the play surrounded by a decorated border. These scenes usually were 'fancy' pictures, having no relation to the play as staged or to the actors in a production.

Hamilton provided several portraits of Mrs Siddons for this series, and broke the general rule by depicting her also in the 'fancy' title scene, when the play he was illustrating was associated with her, and though not representing the play in performance, they are likenesses of the actress.

Cleone, a tragedy by Robert Dodsley (1703-1764) was first produced at Covent Garden in 1758 with George Anne Bellamy in the title role. It was not revived till it was given two performances at Drury Lane in 1786 by John Philip Kemble for Mrs Siddons. The first, on 22 November, so moved and terrified the audience that, it is stated, the ladies stayed away from the second performance 'because of the fearfull Nature of the Play.' It was not performed again.

Despite its title, there is nothing Greek about the play: it is a typical example of the mid-eighteenth century pseudo-Gothic movement. Time and place are unspecified; references to 'the Forest of Baden' suggest a German setting, but the names of the characters are vaguely French-sounding.

Cleone, wandering in the wood, is set upon by Ragozin, a servant, masked and flourishing a dagger. This is the scene in Act III, Scene 3, depicted in the painting (engraved by A Smith 1792):

Ragozin: "Stop! for thou fly'st in vain."
Cleone: "Help! mercy! save!
        Kill not my infant! Murder! O, my child!"

Deaf to her entreaties, Ragozin kills the child and stabs at Cleone, who swoons, apparently dead. When Cleone revives and finds her child dead she goes mad and covers his body with boughs, imagining he is asleep.

14 *Twelfth Night, or What You Will* by William Shakespeare
The Street, with The Duke, Viola, Olivia, and the Priest
Act V, Scene 1
by **William Hamilton**
oil   68 × 86 (26¾ × 34)

This picture is one of the series of paintings commissioned for *The Shakespeare Gallery* by John Boydell, an engraver and publisher. Boydell had by his patronage given employment to English engravers and, having placed their work in the first rank of the art, was determined to do the same for English painting. His plan was to commission illustrations for the works of Shakespeare from the most eminent artists of the period. The original pictures (painted from 1792 to 1801) were engraved and issued in two volumes in 1803. The paintings were exhibited in London at his 'Shakespeare Gallery' in Pall Mall.

Boydell became Lord Mayor of London in 1790. Though his project had undoubted prestige it failed financially, and in 1805, the year after his death, the originals were sold by auction. Some of these are now in the Picture Gallery at the Royal Shakespeare Theatre, Stratford-upon-Avon.

The painting of this scene from *Twelfth Night* was engraved by Francis Bartolozzi RA in 1797. A preliminary oil sketch for the painting is in the Yale Centre for British Art.

15 *Love for Love* Act IV, Scene 1, by William Congreve
by **Robert Smirke**
oil   47.5 diameter (18¾)

This is another of the series of paintings commissioned as title pages for Bell's *British Theatre*, the other being the scene from *Cleone*, **13**.

It is entirely 'fancy' in that it bears no relation to actors or a stage production. The picture represents the scene in *Love for Love* where Valentine feigns madness to prevent the signing away of his real property for the advance of £4,000 in cash to clear his debts. To his lodgings comes his father, Sir Sampson Legend, with Buckram, a lawyer, to obtain Valentine's signature on the deed. Valentine's feigned madness sends Buckram away with the lines:

    "O Lord, let me be gone!
    I'll not venture myself with a madman!"

This quotation is on the engraving by Neagle 1791. The painting is unsigned.

14

12

13 in colour on page *10*

15 in colour on page *11*

16 John Henderson (1746-1785) as Hamlet
Richard Wilson (1744-1796) as Polonius
Hamlet by William Shakespeare
Covent Garden Theatre 1779
by an unknown artist
oil   89 × 69 (35 × 27¼)

The moment is that in Act III, Scene 2, when, following the 'recorder' incident with Rosencrantz and Guildenstern, Hamlet bewilders Polonius with incoherent conversation.

Hamlet: "Do you see yonder cloud, that's almost in the shape of a camel?"
Polonius: "By the Mass, an' 'tis like a camel, indeed."

In the background, one of the players is seen retiring with the recorder.

There is a painting in the Garrick Club of these two actors, three-quarters length, at the same moment in the play, though it differs in details. It is most probably by the same artist.

In the Garrick Club catalogue it is attributed to George Romney, and the actors are named as Henderson and Wilson. While there is no cause to doubt the names of the actors the attribution to Romney is not acceptable. A tentative suggestion has been made that it is the work of Benjamin Wilson.

John Henderson was encouraged to take up the stage as a profession by Garrick and made his first appearance at Bath, under the name of Courtney, in 1772, as Hamlet, at the salary of one guinea a week. He became an 'excellent favourite' in this town, resumed his own name, and was eventually engaged by Colman for the Haymarket, where he made his London debut 1777, as Shylock. He first played Hamlet there on 22 June. He soon appeared at Drury Lane, and then Covent Garden, where he played Hamlet, with Wilson as Polonius, on 26 April 1779. His success was short-lived: he died aged thirty-nine of overwork and the result of early privations and was buried in Westminster Abbey.

Hamlet is depicted in the contemporary eighteenth-century black costume, as worn by all actors in the part till John Philip Kemble introduced the Van Dyck costume in 1783.

17 Jane Barsanti (d 1795) as Signor Arionelli
The Son-in-Law by John O'Keeffe with music by Samuel Arnold
Smock Alley Theatre, Dublin 1782/3
by an unknown artist
watercolour   25.75 × 15.6 (10⅛ × 6⅛)

John O'Keeffe (1747-1833), the Irish dramatist, was first an actor in Dublin for twelve years, but his eyesight began to fail at the age of twenty-three and eventual blindness forced him to leave the stage, though he continued to write farces and light operas. His first play was written at the age of fifteen. Among his best known works are: *The Agreeable Surprise* (1781); *The Castle of Andalusia* (1782); *The Poor Soldier* (1783); and *Wild Oats* (1791).

The Son-in-Law, a musical farce, with music by Samuel Arnold, was first produced on 14 August 1779 at the Haymarket Theatre with Charles Bannister in the part of Arionelli.

It was performed in Dublin at the Smock Alley Theatre in 1782/3. The Dublin edition of the play (1783) gives the cast with no exact date of performance but lists Mrs Daly (Jane Barsanti) as Signor Arionelli.

Jane Barsanti was a member of an Italian musical family who settled in London and were associated with the King's Theatre (the Italian Opera House). She was a pupil of Dr Burney and first appeared at Covent Garden Theatre in 1772. She is said to have been an accomplished singer and actress and remained with the company until 1776, creating Lydia Languish in Sheridan's *The Rivals* in 1775. She also appeared at the Haymarket Theatre in 1777. From June to August she was billed as Miss Barsanti, but from 28 August to 19 September as Mrs Lisley. She was married to John Lisley but it is recorded that her husband's family would not allow her to call herself by her married name on the bills. Lisley died and left her a considerable fortune, and two months later she married the Dublin actor Richard Daly. On the strength of her money he took over the management of the Smock Alley Theatre in 1781 where she appeared with great success. She died in 1795.

The identification of the drawing as Miss Barsanti relies on an inscription on the contemporary mount. It is neither signed nor dated. Originally it was suggested that the part was Arbaces in Dr Arne's opera *Artaxerxes* (by costume, etc) but no record could be found of her playing the part, which was often acted *en travestie*. Genest quotes O'Keeffe in his reminiscences where he records he saw this actress play Arionelli in his *The Son-in-Law* ". . . but, it being her fixed determination never to appear in men's clothes, she dressed the character in the Eastern style, as Arbaces in *Artaxerxes*". He calls her 'Mrs Lister' not Lisley but, as the text of the play shows, she was then acting under the name of Mrs Daly.

18 John Bannister (1760-1836) as Gloucester
John Pinder (17?-1812) as Sir Richard Ratcliffe
Richard III by William Shakespeare
Haymarket Theatre 1794
by an unknown artist
oil   125.5 × 100 (49½ × 39½)

This picture has been variously identified during its history. The character with Richard has also been wrongly given, owing to the fact that the Colley Cibber version of Shakespeare's play was always used in the nineteenth century, and lines given by Shakespeare to one character are differently allotted in the Cibber version.

It is certain that the moment shown is Act V, Scene 8, in the Cibber version, during the battle of Bosworth when Richard calls: "A horse! a horse! My Kingdom for a horse!" and Sir Richard Ratcliffe replies: "This way, this way, my Lord; Below yon thicket stands a swift horse."

This painting has been attributed to Zoffany and William Beechey at various times, both of which attributions are unacceptable. By costume it is most likely that the picture dates from 1794 and represents Bannister and Pinder. Bannister played Gloucester on two occasions, both being Benefits for his father, Charles, at the Haymarket Theatre, the first on 24 August 1791, the second 27 August 1794.

It is suggested that the painting may be by Thomas Parkinson who exhibited between 1769 and 1789, and possibly later. Several of his works have, in the past, been mistaken for those of Zoffany and a comparable battle scene from *Cymbeline*, dated 1778, is in the Garrick Club Collection.

Bannister, who had studied as a painter, was a close friend of many of the artists of the period, and, though Richard was not one of his successes as far as the public was concerned, his vanity may well have been the reason for the picture. He had a high opinion of himself in the part, and nothing would have been simpler for him than to have persuaded one of his friends to execute a portrait. This could be the reason for the departure from the usual pattern, that of actors being painted in their successes.

16

17

18

23

19 George Frederick Cooke (1756-1812) as Gloucester
Richard III by William Shakespeare
copy of a painting by an unknown artist (c 1805)
oil   73 × 61.5 (28¾ × 24¼)

George Frederick Cooke was born in London in 1756 and was
apprenticed to a painter as a youth, but he forsook this profession
for the theatre, making his debut at Brentford in 1776. He first
appeared in small parts in London at the Haymarket in 1778-9, but
for the next twenty years he was a provincial strolling player and
stock actor. It was during these years that he acquired the habit of
intemperance which was to be his downfall. He made a triumphant
return to London, when he appeared at Drury Lane on 31 October
1800 in *Richard III*. Gloucester was to become his most famous
part. Kemble never essayed it again while Cooke was in England
for fear of comparison.

The painting in this collection is a copy, in a more vigorous tech-
nique, of an original portrait which has not been traced, nor has it
been possible to ascertain the name of the artist of this lost original.
It was reproduced as a frontispiece in 1906 to an edition of *Henry
VI, Part 3* without any information. There are several engraved
versions which derive from this lost original, as well as other copies
in oil.

Several artists have been named in association with the Maugham
painting since it came to light in 1916. These include Charles Leslie
and Samuel De Wilde, both of which attributions are untenable.

19

20 *Twelfth Night, or What You Will* by William Shakespeare
Malvolio appearing cross-gartered before Olivia and Maria
Act III, Scene 4
by **Thomas Stothard**
oil   57 × 42.5 (22½ × 16⅜)

This picture was painted by Thomas Stothard as an illustration to
Heath's *Pictorial Shakespeare*, published in 1802. It was engraved
by James Heath, ARA, and is not of an actual stage production.
The engraving is in reverse to the oil painting and differs in minor
details. There is a watercolour in the British Museum print room
which is said to be the work of Stothard and the original for the
engraving. This is the same way round as the engraving and is an
exact copy of it, following the minor changes made between the oil
and the engraving. It is now believed, after careful comparison, that
the oil painting is the original from which the engraving was made,
and that the watercolour was copied from the engraving, either by
Stothard, or another artist, at a later date.

20

28 De Wilde Thomas Collins in *The Merry Wives of Windsor*
see page *32*

25 De Wilde Maria Theresa Bland, Ursula Booth and John Bannister in *The Children in the Wood*
see page *30*

41 see page *38*
42 see page *40*
48 see page *44*
57 see page *50*

41 De Wilde John Fawcett in *The Cabinet*

42 De Wilde Thomas Ludford Bellamy in *Robin Hood*

48 De Wilde Charles Mathews in *The Sleep Walker*

57 De Wilde William Charles Macready in *Richard III*

29 De Wilde Charles Farley in *A Tale of Mystery*
see page *32*

1 Richard Suett (1755-1805) as Colonel Jonathan Oldboy
The School for Fathers (Lionel and Clarissa) by Isaac Bickerstaffe
Drury Lane Theatre 1787
by **Samuel De Wilde**
oil on panel   23 × 18 (9 × 7¼)

Isaac Bickerstaffe's comic opera *Lionel and Clarissa*, with music by
Charles Dibdin, was first produced at Covent Garden in 1768. It
was revised and retitled *The School for Fathers* for the production
at Drury Lane in 1770. The part of Colonel Oldboy was played by
Edward Shuter in the original production: Richard Suett first
played the part when the opera was revived at Drury Lane on
19 December 1787, and continued to do so in revivals.

Charles Dibdin (1745-1814), dramatist, actor, and composer, was
responsible for the music and libretti of some twenty-two ballad
operas and many famous nautical ballads, among them 'Tom
Bowling'. As an actor he created parts in his own works, including
Ralph in *The Maid of the Mill* and Mungo in *The Padlock*. In 1787
he started his famous one-man entertainment in the provinces,
which he brought to London two years later.

Richard Suett was born in 1755, and as a boy sang in the choir of St
Paul's. He first appeared on the stage at Drury Lane in 1780. He
was considered one of the foremost comedians of his day and was
unsurpassed as a Shakespearean clown, though given to over-
grimacing and gagging. He was a great favourite of Charles Lamb,
who called him 'the Robin Goodfellow of the stage'.

This picture, painted about 1790, was engraved by R Woodman in
1808 as a plate to the magazine *The Cabinet*.

21

2 Richard Wilson (1744-1796) as Sir Francis Wronghead
The Provok'd Husband by Colley Cibber
Covent Garden Theatre 1790
by **Samuel De Wilde**
oil   36 × 27 (14¼ × 10¾)

The Provok'd Husband, a comedy by Colley Cibber, was first
produced at the Lincoln's Inn Theatre in 1728, with Robert Wilks
and Nance Oldfield in the parts of Lord and Lady Townley, and
Colley Cibber himself as Sir Francis. The play was a completion of
Vanbrugh's *Journey to London*, which he had left unfinished at his
death in 1726.

Sir Francis is shown in the painting in Act IV, when he is telling
Manly of his attempts to place his daughter at Court and his
appearance in Parliament. The debate was so long-winded that
when the time came to vote, he had forgotten the issue, and when
they came to put the question, he says: "I don't know how 'twas –
but I doubt I cried ay! when I should ha' cried no!"

Richard Wilson made his first appearance at the Haymarket in
1774. He was considered second only to Parsons and Quick as a
portrayer of comedy characters.

The painting is one of a series commissioned by Bell for his *British
Theatre*, and engraved by W Leney in 1791.

22

23 John Palmer (1745-1798) as Don John
The Chances by John Fletcher
Drury Lane Theatre 1791
by **Samuel De Wilde**
oil   37 × 27 (14¼ × 10¾)

The Chances, a comedy by John Fletcher (1579-1625) founded on one of Cervantes' *Novelas Esemplares*, was first produced at The Cockpit in Drury Lane in 1638.

Fletcher is always associated with Sir Francis Beaumont, with whom he wrote several famous plays. Fletcher has also been credited with collaboration with Shakespeare in *The Two Noble Kinsmen*, and it is fairly certain that he was responsible for parts of *Henry VIII*. *The Chances* was revived several times and Don John was a favourite part of Garrick's (in his own version). The moment depicted is Act I, Scene 3, when Don John, returning to his lodging, is intercepted by a woman, who, mistaking him for someone else, hands him a carefully wrapped parcel. On returning home with his booty (which he thinks is treasure) he discovers that it is a live baby.

John Palmer made his first appearance on the stage at the Haymarket in 1766. He later became a member of Garrick's company at Drury Lane. He was the first Joseph Surface in *The School for Scandal* in 1777. Sheridan nicknamed him 'plausible Jack'.

He first played Don John at Drury Lane on 14 May 1782. The painting is signed S De Wilde and dated 1791, and is one of the series commissioned by Bell for his *British Theatre*. It was engraved by Thornthwaite in the same year.

24 John Fawcett (1768-1837) as Jack Nightshade
The Choleric Man by Richard Cumberland, painted 1792
by **Samuel De Wilde**
oil   40 × 30 (15¾ × 11¼)

The Choleric Man by Richard Cumberland (1732-1811) was first produced at Drury Lane in 1774. Cumberland forsook a career in politics in 1761 for that of a dramatist, and wrote a number of mediocre tragedies, but his comedies of a sentimental and domestic character were extremely successful. His play *The Jew* (1794) was the first play sympathetic to the race, and it achieved translation into several languages. Cumberland was extremely sensitive to criticism and was caricatured by Sheridan as Sir Fretful Plagiary in *The Critic*. His work is typical of the kind of play which preceded Sheridan and Goldsmith.

The plot concerns the two sons of Nightshade (the 'Choleric Man' of the title), one educated in town and the other in the country. The picture shows Jack in Act I, Scene 2, when he comes to London to see his brother, who welcomes him kindly, gives him a full purse, and tells him to select an outfit from his own wardrobe. He adds a few words of warning to choose his pleasure discreetly.

"Humph!" Jack says, counting the money, "in all five-and-twenty guineas . . . What was you saying last, brother?"

"Only throwing away a little good advice upon you, Jack – that's all" retorts Charles good-humouredly.

John Fawcett, son of an actor and singer of the same name, was apprenticed to a linen draper, but ran away and made his first appearance on the stage at Margate, under the assumed name of 'Mr Foote'. He eventually joined Tate Wilkinson's company at York in 1787, where his reputation grew, and this secured him an engagement at Covent Garden where he first appeared on 21 September 1791. From this time until the publication of the engraving on 18 February 1793, there is no record of a revival of this play at Covent Garden where Fawcett was continually employed – except for the period between 31 May and 17 September 1792, when the theatre was closed for rebuilding.

During this gap no trace can be found of any London revival of this play, or of Fawcett's activities. It would seem that the part was played by him in the provinces during these months, and this portrait, painted by De Wilde, was engraved by Corner for use as the frontispiece to the edition of the play in Bell's *British Theatre*.

25 Maria Theresa Bland (1769-1838) as Josephine
Ursula Booth (1740-1803) as Winifred
John Bannister (1780-1836) as Walter
The Children in the Wood by Thomas Morton
Haymarket Theatre 1793
by **Samuel De Wilde**
oil   80 × 67 (31½ × 26½)

Thomas Morton (c 1764-1858) wrote numerous sentimental comedies typical of their period. His *The Children in the Wood* was produced at the Haymarket in October 1793. He is best remembered as the creator of 'Mrs Grundy' – a character in *Speed the Plough* (1800) frequently referred to as the embodiment of British respectability, but who does not appear in person on the stage.

The Children in the Wood, a version of the 'Babes in the Wood' story with music by Samuel Arnold (see **18**), was received with acclaim when first produced. The original cast is depicted in the painting. Walter, who has helped abduct the children, repents, concealing them in the wood, but now he cannot find them, and returns to his home where his mother has prepared supper. His despair alarms the old lady, and later, when Josephine (the babes' nurse, and Walter's sweetheart) arrives and tries to cheer him up by singing an old ballad she has just bought from a beggar (about a child murder and a ghost) his agony is at the height. A violent knocking, which is suited exactly to the words of Josephine's song, shakes the cottage. This is the moment shown in the painting.

John Bannister, the son of the actor Charles Bannister, studied art as a youth, but went on the stage in 1778. His successful first appearance at the Haymarket gained him an engagement with Garrick at Drury Lane, where he remained until he retired in 1815.

Maria Bland, the wife of George Bland (brother of Mrs Jordan) was famous as a singer under her maiden name of Romanzini, till she married in 1780. She was with the Drury Lane company for nearly forty years (see **54**).

Ursula Agnes Booth does not seem to have made her first appearance in London until she played in *The Haunted Tower* at Drury Lane in 1790. The painting was exhibited by De Wilde at the Royal Academy in 1794, but was not engraved.

26 Unidentified actor or actress
in an unidentified play, c 1795
attributed to Samuel De Wilde
oil   73.5 × 54 (29 × 21¼)

This painting came into the collection titled 'J. Quick in *The Rivals*' and attributed to De Wilde. It is definitely not John Quick or *The Rivals* but possibly by De Wilde (the reasons are given in *The Artist and the Theatre*).

Unfortunately it has not been possible to identify the sitter either as male or female! 'He' is standing in a garden and wears a glove on 'his' left hand in which 'he' carries the other glove. The motion made by 'his' right hand appears to be that which one would make to indicate the shaking of a dice-box. The costume suggests a young country squire about the date 1795. Possible plays and actors were investigated without success. The figure and the face suggest the possibility that an actress is portrayed. At this period it was fashionable for actresses to delight the town with male impersonations which were said by contemporary critics to be lifelike, though the few pictures that there are of them give the impression that no-one could be deceived by their sex. The problem remains unsolved.

23

24

26

25 in colour on page 26

27 John Bannister (1760-1836) as Sylvester Daggerwood
Richard Suett (1755-1805) as Fustian
Sylvester Daggerwood by George Colman The Younger
Haymarket Theatre 1796
by Samuel De Wilde
oil   83 × 72 (32½ × 28½)

George Colman the Younger (1762-1836) succeeded his father as manager of the Haymarket, which he ran for a number of years, writing and presenting there numerous plays, the best remembered being *The Iron Chest* (1796), *The Heir-at-Law* (1797), and *John Bull* (1803). From 1824 to his death he was Examiner of Plays, and in this office showed a prudery and strictness which were unexpected, considering the tenor of his own work.

Colman wrote a *piece d'occasion* in one act and two scenes for the opening of his management at the Haymarket Theatre on 9 June 1795, under the title of *New Hay at the Old Market*. The cast of seven men and two women included Bannister as Sylvester Daggerwood and Suett as Fustian. The first scene between Daggerwood and Fustian was so successful that it was performed on its own by the same actors for Bannister's benefit at Drury Lane as *A Favourite Scene from the Prelude of 'New Hay'*.

For the following season at the Haymarket Colman revised the piece, turning it into a one-act play called *Sylvester Daggerwood*, produced on 7 July 1796. It remained a successful item for many years.

Its slight plot concerns two men waiting to see the manager of a London theatrical company: one is Daggerwood of 'the Dunstable Company' – a barnstormer trying to arrange for his London debut; the other, Fustian, a seedy playwright who wants to get his tragedy produced.

Daggerwood has been snoozing after his journey, and recites Shakespeare in his sleep. He wakes up with a start when Fustian shakes him and introduces himself:

Daggerwood: "Sir, I am your respectful servant to command, Sylvester Daggerwood, whose benefit is fixed for the eleventh of June, by particular desire of several persons of distinction." (giving him a playbill).

This is the moment in the painting.

There are two versions of the picture: one in the Garrick Club is signed and dated 1797. The Maugham version, signed and dated 1798, differs very slightly. De Wilde exhibited 'Scene in Sylvester Daggerwood' at the Royal Academy in 1778 (? the Garrick Club version). It has not been engraved. The Maugham painting was in the collection of Sir Henry Irving.

28 Thomas Collins (1775-1806) as Slender
The Merry Wives of Windsor by William Shakespeare
Drury Lane Theatre 1802
by Samuel De Wilde
oil   73.5 × 57 (29 × 22½)

The revival of *The Merry Wives of Windsor* on 26 October 1802 had a fine cast. The Falstaff was Stephen Kemble, a very large man, who was able to play the part without padding. Three other famous comedians appeared: Richard Suett as Shallow, John Bannister as Pistol, and William Dowton as Sir Hugh Evans.

Collins, who played Slender, had made his first appearance in London at Drury Lane earlier in 1802. He remained at this theatre during his short career, and died at the age of thirty-one.

The portrait is signed 'S De Wilde', and was exhibited at the Royal Academy in 1803. The head and shoulders were engraved by Ridley in 1804.

29 Charles Farley (1771-1859) as Francisco
A Tale of Mystery by Thomas Holcroft
Covent Garden Theatre 1802
by Samuel De Wilde
oil   89.5 × 69 (35¼ × 27¼)

A Tale of Mystery is founded on a French drama by Pixerécourt called *Coelina ou l'Enfant du Mystère*. Holcroft says in his introduction: 'I cannot forget the aid I received from the French drama from which the principal incidents, many of the thoughts and much of the manner of telling the story are derived.'

It is really a garbled version of the original, but it was the first play in this country to be titled a 'melo-drama'. Holcroft (1744-1809) was at first an actor, but gave up the stage after the success of his first play *Duplicity* in 1781. His most famous play is *The Road to Ruin. A Tale of Mystery* is a true 'Gothic' drama; it is also in the literal sense a 'melo-drama' (ie a play accompanied by music), as at all crucial moments a musical accompaniment underlines the reactions of the characters. The score by Thomas Busby (1755-1838), a distinguished musician, organist, and musical historian, was said, in a contemporary review, to be 'equally entitled to praise for its natural connection with the business of the Drama'.

The 'mystery' in the tale concerns the antecedents of Francisco, the protegé of a rich heiress, Selina. Francisco has been attacked and rendered dumb, but is able to write. In answer to Selina's question: "Do you know the traitors? Who are they?" he writes: "The same who stabbed me among the rocks." (Part of the sentence is clearly visible on the paper in the picture).

Charles Farley made his debut at the age of eleven: later with Charles Dibdin, he was responsible for staging *Harlequin and Mother Goose*, which made Grimaldi's name as Clown. Farley remained in charge of pantomimes at Covent Garden until he retired in 1834.

This painting was exhibited at the Royal Academy in 1803; it has not been engraved.

30 Richard Suett (1755-1805) as Diggery Duckling
Walter Maddocks (17?-18?) as Wat
or
John Purser (1776-1808) as Cymon
Sarah Sparks (1754-1837) as Miss Bridget Pumpkin
Francis Waldron (1744-1818) as Sir Gilbert Pumpkin
Mrs Henry (17?-18?) as Kitty Sprightley
Vincent de Camp (1777-1839) as Captain Charles Stanley
Mr Fisher (17?-18?) as William
George Bartley (1782-1858) as Harry Stukeley
All the World's a Stage by Isaac Jackman
Drury Lane Theatre 1803
by Samuel De Wilde
oil   81 × 93 (32 × 36½)

Isaac Jackman was an Irish gentleman trained for the law. He was joint editor of the *Morning Post* from 1786 to 1795, and wrote a number of comic operas, farces and burlesques between 1777 and 1788, of which *All The World's a Stage* was the most successful. It was first produced at Drury Lane on 7 April 1777, with Baddeley as Sir Gilbert and Priscilla Hopkins as Kitty. The farce satirised the then popular craze for amateur country house theatricals.

Kitty Sprightley, an enthusiastic amateur, ward of Sir Gilbert Pumpkin, is getting up a performance of *The Beggar's Opera* and has written to Sir Gilbert's nephew, Captain Charles Stanley, asking him to play Macheath. During rehearsals, which completely upset the household, Kitty falls in love with Charles and they are secretly married. Just before the performance is to take place, news of it comes to light. Sir Gilbert's anger is only abated when he

30

28 in colour on page *25*

27

29 in colour on page *28*

realises that he can return to domestic peace without 'theatricals', so he gives his blessing.

This is the moment depicted in the painting. At the close of the play, Sir Gilbert has just forgiven the lovers and Miss Bridget, his sister, who has also heard of the elopement, rushes in; the company mistake her anger for playacting. She faints, and on recovery, runs at Diggery, a servant, who has congratulated her on her acting ability. She, too, is pacified, and all ends happily.

The revival depicted in the painting was at Drury Lane on 12 March 1803, when it was performed for the 'first appearance on this stage' of Mrs Henry. Of this actress little can be traced. She does not seem to have acted again till October 1804, then disappears. The painting was titled, when it passed through Christie's in 1939, as of 'Quick and Mrs F A Henry'. 'Quick' proves an error, and no confirmation can be found of the intitials F A, though it seems strange these should have become attached to it without some grounds. The other central figure, Sir Gilbert Pumpkin, is Francis Waldron. He was born in 1744 and first appeared at Drury Lane in 1769 with Garrick, who appointed him manager of the Theatrical Fund. He also ran the theatres at Windsor and Richmond during his long career. He wrote a number of plays and later in life only made occasional appearances on the stage, though he was prompter at the Haymarket as late as 1805.

Vincent De Camp was the brother of Mrs Charles Kemble (see **35**), and for Suett (see **19**). The painting was the last to be acquired by Maugham in 1953 for his theatrical collection. It appears to be unfinished and was not engraved.

---

31 Charles Mathews (1776-1835)
in an unidentified play 1803-4
attributed to **Samuel De Wilde**
oil   75 × 57 (29½ × 22½)

This painting has had a chequered career since 1871 (when it first appeared in the records) as to the identification of the actor and of the artist. Garrick by Zoffany, and Macklin by De Wilde have both been suggested, but there is no doubt that the actor portrayed is Charles Mathews, and that the picture was painted during the first years following his London debut at the Haymarket Theatre in 1803. He was painted many times by De Wilde, and on comparison with other portraits, the same tall, lean figure is shown, and the facial resemblance is striking.

Mathews played many servants and country lads, often wearing old-fashioned clothes. It is this type of character, we feel, that is represented in the picture. He appears to be marking time, and alternately raising his hands to a salute. This would suggest a clumsy new recruit or volunteer. Mathews was famous for the songs he introduced into plays, often not part of the play itself, but interpolated numbers.

Amongst the considerable evidence for this attribution is a playbill for a benefit in 1804, in which Mathews appeared in two pieces:– *Love Laughs at Locksmiths* and *Raising the Wind*. It is especially noted on the playbill that: 'In the course of the evening will be sung the following . . . 'The Drill'd Recruit from the Awkward Squad, by Mr Mathews.'

Other military songs appear to have been in his repertoire. The whole subject is discussed at length in *The Artist and the Theatre*.

32 John Emery (1777-1820) as Robert Tyke
The School of Reform by Thomas Morton
Covent Garden Theatre 1805
by **Samuel De Wilde**
oil   74 × 56.5 (29¼ × 22¼)

The School of Reform, or How to Rule a Husband by Morton was first produced at Covent Garden on 15 January 1805 with a brilliant cast which included, besides Emery, Charles Kemble, Cooke and Munden. The play is a peculiar and somewhat ill-assorted mixture of comedy, sentiment, and melodrama. It has, however, a great acting part in Tyke, of whose creator it was said: 'Garrick never blended tragedy and comedy with happier effect than did Emery in this wonderful performance.'

The plot, even for its day, is one of the most complicated. It concerns the lost heir of Lord Avondale. Tyke, the son of an old retainer, knows the family secrets and when he is brought up before his lordship on a charge of felony there is instant recognition. This is the moment depicted in the painting. "If it should be!" exclaims Tyke, "but, no, it can't be . . . I'm damned, but it's him." And he adds, aside, "Oh then, all's just as nice as ninepence."

John Emery, the son of an actor and an actress, both of whom were at Covent Garden, began his theatrical career in the orchestra of the Brighton Theatre, where his mother had made her stage debut. By the age of fifteen the youngster had developed a skill in playing character parts. In 1798 he was engaged by Covent Garden to succeed Quick in comedy parts. During his career there he played many stage countrymen similar to Tyke, which Hazlitt described as the 'sublime of tragedy in low life.'

There are three versions of the painting, which was first exhibited at the Royal Academy in 1806 (the Maugham painting is believed to be this version and the one engraved by Charles Turner in 1808). The other two versions are in the Garrick Club, and in a private collection in America. There is also a watercolour (see **36**) in the Maugham Collection which is after this picture and probably a copy from the engraving.

---

33 J Field (17?-18?) as Frank
The Three and the Deuce by Prince Hoare, painted 1811/12
by **Samuel De Wilde**
oil   43 × 34 (17 × 13½)

Prince Hoare (1755-1834), son of a portrait painter, was a successful writer of comedies and musical entertainments, which included such favourites in their day as *No Song, No Supper, The Prize, Lock and Key* and *The Three and the Deuce*, a comedy in one act and four scenes, which was first produced at the Haymarket in 1795, with John Bannister in the leading parts of the 'Three Singles', and George Wathen as Frank.

The play was derived from a Spanish comedy, *Los Tres Mellizos* and the parts of the brothers provided a fine opportunity for the comedian who played all these parts.

It chronicles the adventures of triplet brothers – Pertinax, Peregrine, and Percival Single, indistinguishable in appearance but very different in character; Pertinax is responsible and well-behaved, Peregrine is a wild young fellow, while Percival is a half-wit.

The play opens in the dining-parlour of Justice Touchit. Frank, a countryman, complains to the Justice that his sister Phoebe has been compromised by Squire Peregrine Single. Touchit advises him to sound Peregrine tactfully about his intentions, cautioning him, "You'll remember to be genteel?" To which Frank replies, as he leaves, "Oh, I be famous, I tell ye, for a bit of gentility." This is the moment in the painting.

The actor depicted as Frank is definitely known to be Mr Field, but his history and where he played the part is unknown. This picture

32

31

33

was exhibited by De Wilde at the Royal Academy in 1812 as 'Mr Field as Frank in *The Three and the Deuce*,' but there is no London revival of the play in this period in which the name of Field occurs as Frank.

'Mr Field' is undoubtedly the J Field who first appeared at the Haymarket in 1803 and was then at Covent Garden up to 1811. He then disappears from the bills.

It is unusual to find De Wilde exhibiting paintings of minor actors at the Royal Academy – all his pictures there were of more important figures. Field must have been well-known in his day, though unknown to posterity.

34 William Farren (1786-1861) as Lovegold
The Miser by Henry Fielding
Covent Garden Theatre 1818
by **Samuel De Wilde**
oil   74 × 56.5 (29¼ × 22¼)

Henry Fielding (1707-1754) is most remembered as a novelist and the author of *Tom Jones*, but in his early years he wrote a number of works for the theatre – and was for a period lessee of the Haymarket. His adaptation of Molière's *L'Avare* was first produced at Drury Lane in 1733, with Benjamin Griffin in the part of Lovegold.

The play tells of Lovegold, the old miser who wishes to marry Marianne, with whom his son Frederick is in love. To prevent this, Marianne pretends to be extravagant. She orders valuable jewellery, clothes of the most expensive materials. The house is beset by duns at her instigation. This so terrifies Lovegold that he gives her £2,000 to be let out of his bargain, which leaves Marianne free to marry Frederick.

The painting depicts Lovegold in the last scene of Act IV, in an apartment in his house. He has discovered that his money has been stolen, and rages to himself in the utmost distraction:

"Thieves! Thieves! Assassination! Murder! I am undone! All my money is gone! Who is the thief? Where is the villain? Where shall I find him?"

William Farren made his first appearance on the stage at Plymouth in 1806 (as Lovegold). In London his debut was at Covent Garden in 1818 as Sir Peter Teazle, which remained one of his favourite parts. He continued to play, throughout his long career, 'Crusty old bachelors, jealous husbands, storming fathers, worrying uncles, or conceited fops with ghastly pretensions to amiability.' He retired in 1853.

He played Lovegold for the first time at Covent Garden on 3 October 1818 and De Wilde exhibited this painting (signed and dated 1820) at the Royal Academy the same year. It was not engraved.

35 Charles Mathews (1776-1835) as Charles Goldfinch
The Road to Ruin by Thomas Holcroft
by **Samuel De Wilde**, painted 1820
oil   29 × 25 (11½ × 9¾)

The Road to Ruin, first produced at Covent Garden in 1792 with William Lewis as Goldfinch, was the most famous play of Thomas Holcroft (1744-1809) and remained a favourite for many years. It has the usual involved plot: two young men Dornton and Milford are on the 'road to ruin' by their extravagance. Goldfinch, a vulgar horsey fellow, is one of their cronies. He says of himself "Father was a sugar-taker, grandfather a slop-seller. I'm a gentleman." The painting shows him boasting "Ain't I a genius?" Dornton replies, "Quite an original! You may challenge the whole fraternity of the Whip to match you!" And Goldfinch adds: "Match me! Newmarket *can't* match me!"

Charles Mathews, son of a London bookseller, left home and his uncongenial employment to go on the stage. He made his debut in Dublin in 1794. He eventually secured an engagement with Tate Wilkinson at York, and from there he joined the new company George Colman was forming for the Haymarket, which consisted mainly of newcomers to the London stage. Mathews first appeared in 1803. This was the start of a long and successful London career.

His chief hobby was acquiring theatrical paintings. The large collection he made was housed in a special gallery built on to his home – Ivy Lodge, Kentish Town. Unfortunately he was forced by circumstances to offer the pictures for sale in 1833; for this purpose they were shown at the Queen's Bazaar in Oxford Street. Mathews had hoped that these pictures would become the property of the Garrick Club. He did, in fact, before the exhibition, offer them the opportunity of purchasing the collection for £3,000, but the club could not afford this sum. It was not until after Mathews' death in 1835 that the pictures were purchased from his widow by John Rowland Durrant for £1,000. Durrant, a wealthy stockbroker and Founder Member of the Garrick, bought the collection for the club, who were to repay him the capital when convenient. Meantime he received a five per cent interest on his outlay. Durrant died in 1853 before repayment, and in his will he bequeathed the collection to the club as a free legacy. They are still the major part of the famous collection of theatrical paintings housed in the club.

Mathews first played Goldfinch at the Haymarket in 1812 and it remained one of his most famous comedy parts. The De Wilde painting is signed and dated 1820 and has not been engraved. There are other De Wilde paintings of him in this part.

36 Giles Linnett Barrett (d 1795) as Sir Gilbert Pumpkin
All the World's a Stage by Isaac Jackman
Haymarket Theatre 1793
by **Samuel De Wilde**
watercolour   23.35 × 16.5 (9³⁄₁₆ × 6½)

The plot of Isaac Jackman's play has been told (see **30**). Barrett is remembered as an actor and manager of the Norwich Theatre and its circuit from 1784-1788 (he is often confused with Giles *Leonard* Barrett, another actor in London and the provinces, who went to America in 1796 and died there in 1809).

The watercolour is signed and dated 1794. Barrett is recorded as having played Sir Gilbert in a revival of *All the World's a Stage* at the Haymarket Theatre on 24 September and 3 October 1793. This drawing was etched, probably by De Wilde himself, and published by J Tayleure. It is titled 'G. L. Barrett actor and manager of the Norwich Theatre 1782 ob. 1795'.

34

36

35

37 Maria Thérèsa de Camp (1774-1838) as Patie
The Gentle Shepherd, adapted from Allan Ramsay's poem
by Richard Tickell
Drury Lane Theatre 1796
by **Samuel De Wilde**
pencil and watercolour   34.95 × 21.75 (13¾ × 8⁹⁄₁₆)

Allan Ramsay's Scottish pastoral poem, published in 1729, was first adapted for the stage as *Patie and Peggy* by Colley Cibber in 1730 and later by several other hands under various titles. The version 'altered' by Richard Tickell with music by Linley was first seen at Drury Lane in 1781. It remained the accepted version for many years with the convention of Patie (the Gentle Shepherd) being played *en travestie*.

Thomas Linley (1725-1795) was father of the famous Bath family of musicians. He became part owner of Drury Lane Theatre in 1776 with his son-in-law, Richard Brinsley Sheridan. He was responsible for the music for many pieces including *The Duenna* (1775) and the songs in *The School for Scandal* (1777).

Thérèsa de Camp was born in Vienna where she appeared as a child dancer. The family (three sisters and two brothers) came to London. Vincent (see 30) had a successful career in this country from 1793 before he left and went to America in 1823. Thérèsa first appeared in London at Covent Garden Theatre in 1786 and in 1806 married Charles Kemble (becoming the mother of Fanny Kemble). She played Patie in a revival of the play 8 June 1796 at Drury Lane.

The sketch is not signed, but a later hand inscribed it 'Miss De Camp, now Mrs C. Kemble' and as by De Wilde. There is a similar oil-painting, undated, by De Wilde of her in the same part in the Garrick Club Collection. Neither has been engraved.

38 John Emery (1777-1820) as Robert Tyke
The School of Reform by Thomas Morton
Covent Garden Theatre 1805
after **Samuel De Wilde**
watercolour   37.3 × 23.65 (14¹¹⁄₁₆ × 9⁵⁄₁₆)

This is an inferior unsigned watercolour on paper watermarked 1815 and is probably derived from the engraving by Charles Turner published in 1808. Its similarity in shading etc is more clearly associated with this mezzotint than with the versions of the oil painting, one of which is in this collection (see 32).

39 Charles James Mathews (1803-1878) Portrait as a child
'The Little Parson' 1807
by **Samuel De Wilde**
watercolour   23.8 × 18.9 (9³⁄₈ × 7⁷⁄₁₆)

Charles James Mathews, the son of Charles Mathews and his second wife, Anne Jackson, was naturally brought up in a theatrical atmosphere. His father, a great collector and patron of De Wilde, was at the Haymarket Theatre in the year his son was born, on 26 December 1803. In his autobiography, *The Life of Charles James Mathews*, edited by Charles Dickens (son of the novelist), published in two volumes in 1879, Mathews says:

'Beside the familiar sobriquet of 'Twig', I was almost generally spoken of as 'the Little Parson', and, as an appropriate birthday offering, one of our waggish friends presented to me a complete little parson's suit of black – old-fashioned square-cut coat, long flapped waistcoat, knee-breeches, worsted stockings, shoes, and buckles, white bands etc. – attired in which I was lifted on the dining-room table to drink the healths of the 'tompany'. The drawing of me in my clerical costume by De Wilde bears the date of June, 1807, which would make my age at that time just three years and a half, which I fancy may be safely taken as my earliest appearance in character.'

A lithograph of this watercolour was illustrated in the autobiography but the chair is omitted which in the Maugham original emphasises how small Mathews the younger then was.

The date, June, is a mistake as the original is signed and dated July 25, 1807, but there is little doubt that they are one and the same picture.

At the time the book was published the watercolour was said to be in the possession of J L Toole, the actor. After Toole's death in 1906 the picture was bought by Edward Leger, the proprietor and editor of *The Era*. There is a version in oil of the watercolour, also by De Wilde, in the Garrick Club.

40 John Fawcett (1768-1837) as Job Thornberry
John Bull, or The Englishman's Fire-side
by George Colman the Younger
Covent Garden Theatre 1807
by **Samuel De Wilde**
watercolour   36.85 × 23.5 (14½ × 9⁷⁄₈)

George Colman's play was first produced at Covent Garden 5 March 1803 with Fawcett in the part of Thornberry. He played the part again when the play was revived at Covent Garden in April and November 1807.

Job Thornberry is the main character in the play. He is a generous and kind-hearted but irascible man under a sense of injustice, who is supposed to typify the British national character. The story is of his son, who runs away to sea but returns to amass a fortune and become a philanthropist and right previous wrongs. The play, set in the Cornish countryside near Penzance, was an immediate success on its first production achieving 46 performances in its first season. It was still being staged as late as 1872.

The watercolour is signed and dated O(ctober) 1807. It was, at one time, inscribed on a mount: "In one word, will your son marry my daughter? Act V Scene 2nd".

A watercolour of Fawcett in the same character, but seated, is in the Garrick Club Collection, signed and dated Or (October) 1807. This was engraved (in part) as a plate for the magazine *The Cabinet* in 1808. Fawcett (see 24) also wrote a number of successful plays, and a contemporary said 'His comedy had, perhaps, too much mannerism in it but his pathetic was nature's own.'

41 John Fawcett (1768-1837) as Whimsicolo
The Cabinet by Thomas Dibdin
Covent Garden Theatre 1808
by **Samuel De Wilde**
watercolour   37 × 23.3 (14½ × 9³⁄₁₆)

Thomas Dibdin (1771-1844) (see 70) wrote the comic opera *The Cabinet* which had music by William Reeve, John Morehead (17?-1804), Dominico Corri (1744-1825), John Davy (1763-1824), and John Braham (the tenor who played Prince Orlando in the piece). They were all well-known composers of light music of the period.

George Daniel in his 'remarks' in Cumberland's *British Theatre* says: 'The name of this piece is significant of its plot – if the circumstances of a young lady being locked up in a cabinet, and sent back to her lover, may be fairly called one.'

Fawcett (see 24) created the part of the valet, Whimsicolo, and played it in many subsequent revivals.

The watercolour is signed and dated 20 May 1808 and was engraved in colour by Wageman the same year. There are several other engraved versions, one of which bears the quotation "But what, my valiant tale of a lion".

40

38

37

41 in colour on page *27*

39

42 Thomas Ludford Bellamy (1770-1843) as Robin Hood
Robin Hood, or Sherwood Forest by Leonard MacNally
Covent Garden Theatre 1806
by Samuel De Wilde
watercolour   36.85 × 22.85 (14½ × 9)

Leonard MacNally (1752-1820) we are told was 'infamous in Irish history as an informer' and 'a writer of dramatic pieces. He had no real merit.' His comic opera, *Robin Hood*, was set to music by William Shield (1748-1829), a prolific but now forgotten composer who had his first success in 1778 at the Haymarket Theatre with *The Flitch of Bacon.* He became resident composer at Covent Garden from 1778 to 1797 and composed the music for over forty operas, pantomimes and farces. He was later Master of the Royal Music and eventually buried in Westminster Abbey. The tale of the opera, we are also informed in a history of the Irish Theatre, 'was taken from the old legendary ballads, and affects the ancient phraseology. The character of Robin Hood is poorly drawn. Instead of a bold undaunted spirit he dwindles into a sententious pedant with a couple of bass songs in this play'.

Robin Hood was first produced at Covent Garden Theatre on 17 April 1784 with Charles Bannister in the title role. It was revived at the same theatre for the debut of Thomas Bellamy on 6 October 1806. Bellamy, a bass singer, trained as a chorister at Westminster Abbey, appeared on the concert platform until 1794, when he went to Dublin as a stage manager. He became part owner of numerous theatres in Ireland and the English provinces. After his debut at Covent Garden in 1806 he appeared there and at Drury Lane until 1817, after which he became a choir master.

The watercolour is signed and dated June 1808. At one time it was inscribed on a mount "How sweet in the woodlands Duetto Act 1st scene 1st".

43 Charles Mathews (1776-1835) as Buskin
Killing No Murder by Theodore Hook
Haymarket Theatre 1809
by Samuel De Wilde
watercolour   37.3 × 23.35 (14¹¹⁄₁₆ × 9³⁄₁₆)

Theodore Hook (1788-1841) was the son of a composer, James Hook, and was educated at Harrow and Oxford. He had his first play, *The Soldier's Return*, acted at Drury Lane in 1805. This was followed by some seventeen 'operatic farces' and 'musical pieces'. After a short and disastrous career as a Government official, Hook became editor of *John Bull*, a newspaper, and wrote numerous poems, satires and biographies. His reputation as a wit made him the idol of his contemporaries.

His *Killing No Murder*, with music by his father, James Hook (1746-1827), was produced at the Haymarket Theatre 21 August 1809 with Mathews (see **31** and **35**) as Buskin and John Liston as Apollo Belvi (see **73** and **75**).

It has the usual involved plot. The play opens with Tup, the landlord of the London Inn, and his sister Fanny welcoming a coachload of passengers. Among the arrivals is an actor, Buskin, who greets Fanny with flirtatious gallantry. She wants to marry him, but he has no money and her brother is trying to make a match for her with Apollo Belvi, the young dancing master, a 'consummate coxcomb', a strange mixture of 'boor and beau'. In the second act Apollo Belvi appears and recognises Buskin as an old friend. He recounts his adventures since they last met. He has dabbled in many professions, including the law and the stage, and has now become a dancing master. This part was created by Liston (see **73**).

There are two copies of the watercolour of Mathews. The Maugham one was in the collection of the younger Mathews, and another, now in the Royal Shakespeare Theatre Collection at Stratford-upon-Avon, belonged to the Royal Dramatic College (it is signed and dated April 20th, 1815). Another similar version is in the Garrick Club Collection, signed and dated September 15, 1809.

44 James Grant Raymond (1771-1817) as The Stranger
The Stranger, or Misanthropy and Repentance
by August von Kotzebue
Lyceum Theatre 1810
by Samuel De Wilde
watercolour   36.5 × 22.85 (14³⁄₈ × 9)

Kotzebue (1761-1819), a German dramatist, wrote some 218 dramatic pieces in various forms. He dominated the German theatre during his lifetime and translations of his plays remained in the repertoire both on the continent and in this country for many years. His *Pizarro* was adapted by Sheridan and *Menschenhass und Reue*, written in 1789, was translated into many versions and held the stage for a long period. The most famous translation as *The Stranger* was by Benjamin Thompson (?1776-1816) who adapted many of Kotzebue's works for the English stage.

The Stranger was produced at Drury Lane Theatre 24 March 1798 with John Philip Kemble in the title role and Sarah Siddons as Mrs Haller. The plot is melodramatic and takes place in a German country village, where a stranger is living in exile. He has decided to forget his unhappy past life and lives quietly helping deserving cases in the village. Mrs Haller, housekeeper to the Count and Countess of Wintersen, who live at a nearby castle, is also known for her kindness to deserving villagers, but in reality she is no less than a countess in disguise, who some years earlier was seduced by a worthless villain, and in consequence deserted her husband and children. In the last act she is suddenly faced by The Stranger who proves to be her husband. She nobly provides written evidence that she is the guilty party and offers him a divorce in case he wishes to re-marry. A happy ending is devised when their children suddenly appear, in an emotional reconciliation.

The play was revived many times in London as late as 1891. James Raymond played The Stranger, with Jane Pope as Mrs Haller, at the Lyceum Theatre on 2 October 1810, when the Drury Lane Company were playing at this theatre after the Theatre Royal had been burnt down the previous year.

Raymond came to London from Dublin, where he had achieved some success, to make his first appearance at Drury Lane Theatre as Earl Osmond in *The Castle Spectre* in 1799. He played Macbeth and Hamlet, among other leading parts, in London up to 1811. He appeared in Bath in 1814 and seems then to have disappeared. He died in 1817.

The watercolour, signed and dated November 1810, shows The Stranger, towards the end of the play, (Act V Scene 2) when he is confronted with his wife:

The Stranger: "No confession, Madam! I release you from every humiliation. I perceive you feel we must part forever."

45 William Dowton (1764-1851) as Dr Cantwell
The Hypocrite by Isaac Bickerstaffe
Lyceum Theatre 1812
by Samuel De Wilde
watercolour   37.15 × 24.8 (14? × 9¾)

Isaac Bickerstaffe (see **4**) adapted Colley Cibber's *The Non Juror* (1717) founded on Molière's *Tartuffe*, as *The Hypocrite*, with Thomas King as Dr Cantwell (Tartuffe). It remained the accepted version of the play and was revived as late as 1887. William Dowton first played Dr Cantwell at Drury Lane Theatre in 1804 and it became one of his most famous parts. It was said – 'Dowton's Doctor Cantwell is a masterpiece of pious dissimulation. His eyes alternately lifted up in holy rapture, and cast down in humility and self-abasement, his subdued tone of voice, his half-suppressed sighs, his crocodile tears, were admirably in character.' He made his first appearance in London at Drury Lane in 1795 and remained

42 in colour on page *27*

43

44

45

before the public until he retired in 1840. He was also famous for his Sir Anthony Absolute, Falstaff and Mr Hardcastle (see **49**).

Dowton played Dr Cantwell in a revival of the play at the Lyceum Theatre (The Drury Lane Company) on 12 and 19 March, and 8 April 1812. There are three watercolours by De Wilde of him in this part, all dated May 1812. One is in the British Museum, another is in the collection of Ian Mayes, and the third is in the Maugham Collection. An old inscription at the base of this water-colour confirms the identification and date. There is an engraving of Dowton in *The Hypocrite* after De Wilde, engraved in September 1822 and included in Terry's *The British Theatrical Gallery* (1825); this is not from any of these watercolours: Cantwell does not have a book in his hands, and he is wearing a dark wig.

---

46 Richard Jones (1779-1851) as Young Contrast
The Lord of the Manor by John Burgoyne
Covent Garden Theatre 1812
by **Samuel De Wilde**
watercolour   37.3 × 22.75 (14¹¹/₁₆ × 9)

John Burgoyne (1722-1792) playwright, author and military man, wrote *The Maid of the Oaks* (1774), *Richard Coeur de Lion* (a translated libretto for Grétry's opera, 1785), and *The Heiress* (1786). His most remembered work is *The Lord of the Manor*, a comic opera, with music by William Jackson, first produced at Drury Lane Theatre 27 December 1780. (John Palmer created the part of Young Contrast).

Burgoyne's military career, rising to a general and a 'meritorious and gallant officer' was marred by an 'ungenerous persecution by the politicians of his day'. He was more successful as a playwright than as a general in North America. William Jackson (1730-1803) composer and organist wrote little for the theatre: most of his life was spent in Exeter where he became organist and choirmaster at the Cathedral.

The Lord of the Manor remained a 'stock' piece for many years, in various adaptations, up to the eighteen-thirties. It has the usual involved plot.

Sir John Contrast, a wealthy landowner and widower, has two sons. The elder has married beneath him, against his father's wishes, and been disinherited, leaving home to settle in another part of the country under the name of Rashley. The play opens some twenty years after these events. Rashly is now a successful farmer, whose wife has died leaving him with two daughters, Sophia and Annette, who have been well educated. The inevitable happens. The local manor house becomes vacant and is bought by old Sir John. Thus unknowingly he becomes his son's landlord. Sir John arrives to meet his tenants with his younger son, a charming but foolish coxcomb. Young Contrast meets Sophia in the village and falls in love with her, unaware of the fact that she is his niece! Rashly, when he finds out, decides to leave, but before he can, Sir John decides to pay the farm a visit. Rashly makes a hasty retreat, leaving his daughters to entertain his father, who is charmed by such young ladies, unlike the usual villagers. They are all invited up to the manor house that evening.

Meantime there is a village fête in progress and the army arrive on manoeuvres and begin recruiting. Young Contrast, on his way to meet Sophia, is mistaken for a deserter and his accoutrements of shako and satchel are put on over his own clothes by the Corporal and Moll Flagon, an old camp follower (a *travestie* part made famous originally by Richard Suett and later John Liston). This is the scene in Act III Scene 4 in the oil painting by De Wilde of which this solo watercolour of Contrast is a part.

Young Contrast: "Why, only hear me, I am a man of fashion."

The play ends when the soldiers take their prisoner before the Lord of the Manor (Sir John) for punishment, and everyone arrives at the house to be recognised, forgiven and reunited.

Richard Jones was trained as an architect in his native Birmingham, but circumstances ordained that he become a provincial actor. He made a name for himself in Dublin and was engaged for Covent Garden Theatre where he made his debut as a light comedian in 1807, without much success. He eventually established himself in 'fop' roles, but he seems always to have had enemies. *Oxberry's Dramatic Biography* (1825) says: 'The lovers of detraction have long since put forth a tale that Mr Jones's figure is made up. This is not the fact. We are aware that Mr Macready's calves take off and on, like Lieutenant Hawke's wooden legs; but Mr Jones's form is from Nature's manufactory; and perhaps she never yet turned out a more elegant specimen of what a man's figure should be.'

One of his biggest successes was Young Contrast in *The Lord of the Manor*, a part he was still playing in 1826. George Daniels in his 'Remarks' on the play says: "But the Young Contrast of Mr Jones – a performance *unique* of its kind – so highly elaborated, and so exquisitely finished, as to leave nothing either to conceive, or to execute."

Richard Jones, often called 'Gentleman Jones', first played the part of Young Contrast when the piece was revived at Covent Garden Theatre 24 October 1812 (and again in 1813 and 1814). De Wilde's painting of the scene from the play (with John Liston as Moll Flagon, Jones as Young Contrast and Hammerton as Sergeant Crimp) was exhibited at the Royal Academy in 1814. This oil painting is now in the Garrick Club Collection. The figure of Jones is *exactly* the same as in the Maugham watercolour, which is neither signed nor dated. It may be a later version by De Wilde made for the actor himself. Another watercolour of Jones in a different act of the play, is also in the Garrick Club Collection, signed and dated 1813, and was etched by De Wilde (see **47**). A portrait of Jones by De Wilde was exhibited at the Royal Academy in 1813, and may have been this watercolour. It is possible that **46** is a solo study for the later full scene, but the similarity is too exact not to assume that the watercolour is copied from the oil.

---

47 Richard Jones (1779-1881) as Young Contrast
The Lord of the Manor by John Burgoyne
Covent Garden Theatre 1812
by and after **Samuel De Wilde**
hand coloured etching   35.9 × 22.75 (14⅛ × 8¹⁵/₁₆)

This picture was originally framed with a mount and thought to be a watercolour, but when unframed in 1966 an inscription in ink was discovered: 'drawn from life and etched by S De Wilde'. This was proved correct on its later cleaning.

De Wilde did several etchings of his own watercolours (Barrett, **36**, in this collection is an example.) They are usually hand-coloured, probably by the artist himself, and titled. This particular etching may be a proof before title.

The original watercolour of Jones in this part is in the Garrick Club Collection, signed and dated 1813.

Young Contrast is depicted in Act I Scene 1 on his entrance with a parasol in one hand and a gun in the other:

Young Contrast: "The Manors are parched to desolation, the saddles are gridirons and the air is impregnated with scurf and freckle; in another half hour I shall be a mulatto in spite of my parasol, by all that's sultry."

46

47

48 **Charles Mathews** (1776-1835) as Somno
The Sleep Walker, or Which is the Lady?
by Wally Chamberlaine Oulton
Haymarket Theatre 1812
by **Samuel De Wilde**
watercolour   36.85 × 22.6 (14½ × 8⅞)

Wally Chamberlaine Oulton (1770-1820) was an Irish author who wrote numerous farces, interludes and burlettas for the Dublin theatre from 1783, none of which reached the London stage. He came to London in 1786, but though he continued to work up to 1817, (his last piece *Frighten'd to Death* was produced at Drury Lane Theatre in February 1817 (see **54**)) his biggest success was *The Sleep Walker, or Which is the Lady?* (first titled *The Twin Sisters, or Forgery in Love*) which was produced at the Haymarket Theatre 15 June 1812, with Mathews (see **35**) in the part of Somno.

The plot concerns Sophia, a runaway heiress, and her lover Sir Patrick M'Guire (later to become her husband). Accompanying them is Somno, an unsuccessful actor turned servant to Sir Patrick. Since leaving the stage, he has taken to sleep-walking and acting famous roles he would never have had the opportunity to perform on stage. There are many added confusions to the plot, including that of Sophia being disguised as a young man; but all end happily, Somno having the last words:

"Let me behold my friends with smiling countenances and my dreams of having met with great applause will be realised. Then Somno may venture to come forward and say Ladies and Gentlemen – 'born for the use and live but to oblige you', and with your permission, the Sleep-Walker will endeavour to entertain you on a future night."

The moment depicted in the picture is in Act II Scene 1, when Somno enters, sleep-walking and 'acting' –

Somno: "Lie there my sword." (lays the candlestick and dressing box on the table).

Mathews was a big success in the part. In the preface to an edition of the play, Oulton thanks Mathews for 'being awake to all the eccentricities of a sleep-walker' and adds that the idea of introducing a somnambulist in comic situations occurred to him from reading curious accounts of sleep-walking in *The Wonders of Nature and Art*.

Mathews was painted by De Wilde in the part and the oil was exhibited at the Royal Academy in 1813; it is now in the Garrick Club Collection. This painting was engraved by J Thompson for *The Theatrical Inquisitor*, August 1816 (this includes the background as in the original oil). The Maugham watercolour is signed and dated September 20, 1814, and is an exact copy of the figure (without background) in the oil original.

49 **William Dowton** (1764-1851) as Hardcastle
She Stoops to Conquer, or The Mistakes of a Night
by Oliver Goldsmith
Drury Lane Theatre 1813
by **Samuel De Wilde**
watercolour   38 × 23.2 (14¹⁵⁄₁₆ × 9¼)

Oliver Goldsmith (1730-1774) was born in Ireland, made his name as an essayist, poet and novelist (particularly with *The Vicar of Wakefield*) before he turned to play writing. It was his second play, *She Stoops to Conquer*, produced at Covent Garden Theatre in 15 March 1773, that became one of the established eighteenth-century comedies side by side with those of Sheridan. His other plays are *The Good Natur'd Man* (1786) and *The Grumbler* (1773).

The story is about two young gallants, Marlow and Hastings, who mistake a country house, which they are going to visit, (belonging to Mr and Mrs Hardcastle) for a country inn. Kate Hardcastle, the daughter of the house, pretends to be a servant and in this guise wins the love of young Marlow who is incapable of passion except below stairs. Her father, unaware of the deception, is furious when treated by Marlow as though he were the landlord of an inn. The moment depicted in the picture is in Act II Scene 1.

Hardcastle: "Zounds! he'll drive me distracted if I contain myself longer. Mr Marlow, sir, I have submitted to your insolence for more than four hours, and I see no likelihood of its coming to an end. I'm now resolved to be master here, sir, and I desire that you and your drunken pack may leave my house directly."

Dowton (see also **45**) became famous for his portrayal of irascible old men and was a famous Sir Anthony Absolute in *The Rivals*. He first played Hardcastle at Drury Lane Theatre on 30 December 1813. The watercolour is not signed or dated but the paper is watermarked 1813. Sale records at one time on the frame (now removed) record ownerships in 1847 and 1881 but gave no precise identification of the subject.

50 **Charles Taylor** (1781-1847) as Noodle
Tom Thumb by Kane O'Hara
Covent Garden Theatre 1815
by **Samuel De Wilde**
watercolour   37.95 × 23.8 (14¹⁵⁄₁₆ × 9⅜)

Henry Fielding (see **34**) was twenty-three when he first wrote *The Tragedy of Tragedies, or the Life and Death of Tom Thumb the Great* as a satire on the old-fashioned and bombastic absurdity of many of the still popular plays which held the stage at that date. It was revised and produced at the Little Theatre in the Haymarket 24 April 1730.

The plot is founded on a legend which is probably of Anglo-Saxon origin about Tom Thumb, the name of a very diminutive little man in the court of King Arthur, killed by the poisonous breath of a spider in the reign of King Thunstone, the successor of Arthur. The play was revised and brought up to date as *Tom Thumb* a 'burletta' (a play with interpolated songs) by Kane O'Hara (1714?-1782) an Irish satirist, who wrote a similar piece, *Midas* (1764) burlesqueing Italian opera, which also remained popular for many years. *Tom Thumb* with music 'composed and compiled' by J Markordt was first produced at Covent Garden Theatre 3 October 1780.

George Daniels in an introduction to the play says – 'To the scholar who understands the full intent and application of the satire *Tom Thumb* will prove a high comic treat; while so exact and ludicrous are the similes – so inflated and bombastical the language – the characters moreover, have such a strutting dignity, and the action is withall so ridiculous and solemn that the public in general can hardly miss the joke, though unacquainted with the absurdities it is intended to laugh at.'

Charles Taylor was a popular singer and actor who first appeared in London at the Haymarket Theatre in 1803. He sang in many of the ballad operas which were part of the stock repertoire of the day. He first played Noodle when the play was revived at Covent Garden Theatre in 1809 and continued to do so in subsequent revivals. Noodle and Doodle are two courtiers in King Arthur's palace. It is Noodle who had Act II Scene 1 all to himself.

Noodle: "Sure, nature means t'unhinge the solid globe! Chaos is come again – all topsy-turvey!"

He then sings:
    "King Arthur in love ankle deep – speed the plough,
    Glumdacla will soon be his punk-a;
    Good Queen Dollalolla's as drunk as a sow,
    And a bed with Tom Thumb,
        Huncamunca."

The watercolour is signed and dated March 1815, and was originally titled on the mount. There is a similar undated watercolour in the Garrick Club collection.

49

50

48 in colour on page *27*

51 John Pritt Harley (1786-1858) as Pedrillo
The Castle of Andalusia by John O'Keeffe
Lyceum Theatre 1815
by **Samuel De Wilde**
watercolour   36.5 × 23.7 (14³⁄₈ × 9⁵⁄₁₆)

O'Keeffe's comic opera with music by Samuel Arnold (see **18**) was first produced at Covent Garden Theatre 2 November 1782 (Pedrillo was played by John Edwin). It was a revised version of *The Banditti, or Love's Labyrinth*, which had been produced at Covent Garden on 28 November 1781 and had been a failure. But with the encouragement of Harris, the manager of the theatre, O'Keeffe and Dr Arnold set to work on a new version which, when produced the following year, achieved instant success and remained a popular favourite for many years. It has the usual involved plot of mistaken identities in which every main character is either impersonating, or being mistaken for, somebody else.

Through the many intrigues of Spado, a bandit (see **76**) it would appear that Don Fernando and his valet, Pedrillo, have decided to exchange roles (but have not done so). When they make their entrance the valet is treated with the utmost courtesy. This is the moment depicted in the picture (Act I Scene 4) when Pedrillo arrives with a portmanteau and is mistaken for his master in disguise.

Pedrillo: "Oh dear! I've got among the gentlefolks! I ask pardon."

The piece was revived at the Lyceum Theatre by the Drury Lane Company on 19 July 1815, with Harley as Pedrillo during his first London season.

John Pritt Harley was a stagestruck youth apprenticed to a linen draper, but as soon as he was free from his indentures, joined Thomas Trotter's Company at the Southend Theatre in 1806. He came to London from the Theatre Royal, Brighton, with a good provincial reputation and made his first appearance at the Lyceum Theatre on 15 July 1815. He remained a favourite comedian, particularly as servants, valets, and the Shakespearean clowns, for the rest of his long career, which lasted right up to his death.

The watercolour is signed and dated August 1815. It was not engraved.

---

52 Eliza O'Neill (1791-1872)
in Character? 1816
by **Samuel De Wilde**
watercolour   18.1 × 16.85 (7¹⁄₄ × 6⁵⁄₈)

The chalk and watercolour sketch is inscribed DW 1816 and an old note on the reverse (now obscured) gave the subject as Miss O'Neill. There is a drawing in watercolour and chalk of a similar style, of a lady in a white cloth headdress, in the Garrick Club collection. It is signed and dated 1815. It came via the De Wilde family and was said to be of Mrs Siddons and drawn from the pit. Sarah Siddons (1755-1831) retired officially in 1812, though she made a number of reappearances in 1813 but, according to her biographers, did not appear in London in 1815 (playing only a number of performances from November in Edinburgh).

There is another associated drawing of a similar lady holding a lyre, also said to be Mrs Siddons, in the possession of Ian Mayes. In the Maugham sketch the head (also in a white cloth 'turban') is seen slightly from below (as in the Garrick Club sketch) and the identification as Eliza O'Neill is more probable, as Mrs Siddons would be in her fifties and Miss O'Neill twenty-four.

Eliza O'Neill made her debut in Ireland, where she made a name for herself, and was engaged for Covent Garden Theatre in 1814 and first appeared as Juliet on 6 October with great success. For the next five years she was the great attraction at Covent Garden Theatre in opposition to Edmund Kean at Drury Lane Theatre. She was considered the natural and worthy successor to Mrs Siddons. Her great parts were Belvidera in *Venice Preserv'd* and Mrs Haller in *The Stranger*. It was in the latter part that she made her farewell appearance 13 July 1819 when she retired to marry William, later Sir William, Becher.

---

53 George Smith (1777-1836) as Schampt
The Woodman's Hut by W H Arnold
Drury Lane Theatre 1816-17
by **Samuel De Wilde**
watercolour   37.8 × 23.7 (14⁷⁄₈ × 9⁵⁄₁₆)

W H Arnold (dates unknown) wrote other melodramas beside *The Woodman's Hut* including *The Devil's Bridge* (1812) but has, in many reference books, been confused with Samuel James Arnold (1774-1852) a much more prolific playwright. As recently as 1975 *The Woodman's Hut* was credited to S J Arnold by a respected American professor. The sorting out of this confusion is not for these pages – and must be left to other hands.

The Woodman's Hut, or The Burning Forest was produced at Drury Lane Theatre, 12 April 1814, with music by Charles Horn (1786-1849). Horn was a singer, composer and musical director, who eventually settled in America where he died. He was also associated with Arnold and John Braham in the music for *The Devil's Bridge*.

The involved plot of *The Woodman's Hut* concerns kidnapping and robbery. Amelia, daughter of the late Count Conenberg, had been kidnapped by the wicked Baron Hernhausen but had escaped and been rescued in the forest by a poor widow and her daughter and given protection in their cottage, a woodman's hut.

The play opens a few years later. The Baron, believing Amelia to be dead, is plotting to kidnap Amelia's cousin Ferdinand, nephew of the late Count who has now inherited the title and the castle. The rest of the play takes place during one night. Amelia and Ferdinand have met and fallen in love. After many adventures they are faced by the Baron's band of robbers, by a river-side. The robbers are led by Schampt, who challenges Ferdinand.

Schampt (levelling a pistol at Amelia): "Withdraw your arms or she dies!"

This is the moment depicted in the picture. Schampt turns his head to motion one of the robbers to seize Amelia but Ferdinand fires: Schampt is wounded and falls to the ground. Amelia rushes forward and secures his pistol and covers the robbers; Ferdinand dashes to her rescue, just as the forest fire, started by the Baron, encroaches. The lovers escape in a convenient boat, leaving the robbers to perish in the burning forest.

George Smith, a singer and actor, was in St Paul's Choir and came to the stage after his voice broke. As a young man he appeared at the Royal Circus and Sadler's Wells Theatre (1803-5). He joined Charles Dibdin in Dublin for a season and came to Drury Lane Theatre in October 1807. He remained a popular bass singer on the stage and concert platform until his death. He is often confused with Richard John Smith, known as 'O' Smith, and their portraits wrongly catalogued.

The watercolour is signed and dated January 1817. It was engraved (three-quarter length) with substantial changes to both the hair and facial expression, by Thompson as the frontispiece to the play in Oxberry's *The New English Drama*, 1822. There seems no explanation for these major differences.

51

53

52

54 Maria Theresa Bland (1769-1838) as Patty
Frighten'd to Death! by Wally Chamberlaine Oulton
Drury Lane Theatre, 1817
by **Samuel De Wilde**
watercolour   37 × 23.35 (14⅝ × 9³⁄₁₆)

Wally Oulton, author of *The Sleep Walker* (see **48**), had his last recorded work, a musical farce, *Frighten'd to Death!* produced at Drury Lane Theatre 27 February 1817. It was founded on a piece, *The Haunted Castle*, which he had written when he was thirteen. This was performed in Dublin, with music by Tommaso Giordani (1744-1816?), who managed an opera company at the Chapel Street Theatre, in December 1783. It was revised by several other hands for its London production, for which help the author gives acknowledgement in his introduction to the published play.

Thomas Simpson Cooke (1782-1848) who wrote the new music was also born in Dublin. He was a tenor singer, conductor and composer at the Smock Alley Theatre from 1797 until he came to London in 1813. He wrote a large amount of light music (see **59**) and was musical director, at times, of Drury Lane and Covent Garden, as well as being a popular singer.

Maria Bland (née Romanzini) (see **25**) who created the part of Patty was a well-loved ballad singer for many years. She was married to George Bland (also a singer) the brother of Dorothy Jordan. Although she played leading roles, she is remembered for the small singing parts often introduced into melodramas, burlettas and musical farces popular in her day. She was with the Drury Lane Company for most of her career. In 1824 she became mentally disturbed, and was cared for by her profession up to her death.

The plot of *Frighten'd to Death!*, a naïve early black comedy, takes place in London on two successive nights and is concerned with Jack Phantom, a young gentleman of dissipated habits. After a rowdy drinking party, one of his companions knocks him unconscious. Emily, the girl with whom he is in love, takes this opportunity to try and cure him. While he is still unconscious, she and several of their friends, including Patty, her companion, drape him in a shroud and place him in a coffin. When he regains consciousness, they treat him as a ghost and nearly frighten him to death. In the end he is cured of his habits and all ends happily.

The piece, with John Pritt Harley as Phantom, was a great success and repeated numerous times in its first season but was soon forgotten.

The moment depicted in the watercolour is Patty's song:
  "Whenever a lad that's good humour'd and free
  Entreats as a lover to choose him,
  I vow in good faith I can't possibly see
  What reason I'd have to refuse him".

The watercolour is signed and dated 1817, and is identified on the reverse as Mrs Bland.

55 John Pritt Harley (1786-1858) as Amoroso
Amoroso, King of Little Britain by James Robertson Planché
Drury Lane Theatre 1818
by **Samuel De Wilde**
watercolour   37.5 × 23.65 (14¾ × 9⁵⁄₁₆)

James Robertson Planché (1796-1880), a prolific dramatist mainly of burlesques and extravaganzas, was also famous for his reforms in historical theatre costumes, and later spectacular staging, particularly in association with Madame Vestris at the Lyceum Theatre in the 1840s. He wrote opera libretti (including *Oberon* for Weber) and English versions of *William Tell* and *The Magic Flute*. He was also Rouge Croix Pursuivant of Arms and later Somerset Herald at the Royal College of Heralds. His book on the *History of British Costume* (1834) was for long a standard work. His autobiography (1872) is a mine of information on its period. In it he says that he was a stagestruck boy who turned amateur actor at the private theatres that abounded in London at the time. He wrote and played the lead in a burlesque *Amoroso, King of Little Britain* 'which being completed and handed round amongst my brother amateurs, was by one of them shown to Mr Harley, of the Theatre Royal, Drury Lane. That establishment happened to be at the moment in a state of absolute starvation – the only cause I can imagine of its sudden snapping at so humble a morsel. Snap at it, however, it did . . . This to me most unexpected event (I knew nothing of its being in the theatre before I saw it announced in the bills for performance) occurred on 21 April 1818, and at once determined my future.'

He later adds that the play was not called by him a burlesque, but 'A Serio-comic, Bombastic Operatic Interlude'. (The music for the piece was written by Thomas S Cooke (see **54**)). Planché also says that George Daniel in his remarks to Cumberland's edition of the piece wrote: 'We have heard that the original title was *Amoroso, King of Pimlico* but the licenser objected to it, in consequence of the palace of a portly potentate being situate in the vicinity.' 'I never heard of such a title, or such a prohibition. The piece was announced without my knowledge, as *The King and the Cook* to which I strongly objected, and insisted upon the restoration of my own title'.

The style is reminiscent of Kane O'Hara's *Tom Thumb* and satirises the foolishness of operatic situations and plots: Amoroso is in love with Mollidusta. Roastando, his cook, is in love with the Queen of Little Britain (Pimlico). Mollidusta (a chambermaid) is in love with Blusterbus, who is a yeoman of the guard. The King sees Roastando salute the Queen with a kiss – he discharges Roastando, but the Queen sees the King and Mollidusta together. She stabs Mollidusta, and the King stabs the Queen: Roastando stabs the King and the King stabs Roastando. Nevertheless, all the dead persons come to life again for the finale:

  "Now take hands and banish sorrow
  Your applause we fain would borrow
  And, if we made you laugh out-right
  Come smile on us tomorrow night."

The moment depicted in the watercolour is Amoroso singing:

  "Her cheek for ever smiling
  Merrily oh! Merrily oh!
  Ev'ry youthful swain beguiling
  Merrily oh! Merrily oh!

Harley (see **51**) who created the part, was originally identified on the reverse of the picture, which is neither signed nor dated. (The paper is watermarked 1817). It was not engraved.

54

55

56 William Farren (1786-1861) as Lord Ogleby
The Clandestine Marriage by David Garrick and
George Colman the Elder
Covent Garden Theatre 1818
by **Samuel De Wilde**
watercolour   37.5 × 23.5 (14¾ × 9¼)

Garrick and Colman's play was first produced at Drury Lane
Theatre 20 February 1766 with Thomas King as Lord Ogleby. It
was a great success and has remained in the repertoire to this day.

George Colman (1732-1794) was the author of many successful,
but now forgotten, plays as well as being associated with the
management of Covent Garden Theatre and then the Haymarket
Theatre, which he acquired from Samuel Foote in 1776, remaining
there till 1789 when he was forced to retire in favour of his son,
George Colman the Younger (see **27**).

The Dramatic Souvenir (1833) says: 'With respect to the parts of
this Comedy written by each author, it was generally supposed that
Garrick produced Lord Ogleby and the courtly personages; and
that Colman wrote the parts of Sterling, and the city family. It is
stated, however, that Colman declared that Garrick, having
composed two acts of this piece, brought them to him, desiring him
to put them together, or do what he would with them, to which
Colman added that he did put them together – into the fire, and
wrote the play alone. He observes in his Preface that though
different parts of the piece were attributed to its authors by both
friends and enemies, each considered himself responsible for the
whole.'

The story is of an elderly decrepit lord arriving in the country in
search of a wife, his adventures with the socially pretentious
Sterlings and eventual discomfiture make up the play.

William Farren (see **34**) first played Ogleby at Covent Garden on
18 September 1818 and it remained one of his famous parts. (He
played it at his farewell in 1851). There are several watercolours,
by De Wilde, of him in the play. One in the Victoria and Albert
Museum (three-quarter length, holding a rose) was engraved by
Hopwood in 1818. Those in the Garrick Club and the Maugham
Collection are a similar pose. The latter is signed and dated
5 January 1819. Neither was engraved.

Lord Ogleby is depicted in the Garden Scene, Act II Scene 2 when
Sterling is showing him his landscaped park:

Ogleby: "What steeple's that we see yonder, the parish church, I
suppose?"

There is also an engraving after De Wilde of Farren in the famous
dressing room scene when Ogleby is prepared for the day by his
valet.

57 William Charles Macready (1793-1873) as Gloucester
Richard III by William Shakespeare
Covent Garden Theatre 1820
by **Samuel De Wilde**
watercolour   37.5 × 23 (14¾ × 9¹⁄₁₆)

Macready made his first appearance in London at Covent Garden
Theatre on 16 September 1816, as Orestes in *The Distressed
Mother*, engaged by the theatre for five years, having previously
made a name in the provinces where he made his debut in 1810.

The Covent Garden management were to use him as a counter
attraction to Kean at Drury Lane, after the retirement of Eliza
O'Neill (see **52**). Though the fortunes of the theatre were at a low
ebb, Macready personally was a great success and, in 1819, they
appointed him leading tragedian and chose Gloucester in
Richard III for his debut in that capacity. Macready was not
anxious to pit himself against Kean in his most famous role, feeling
unsuited for the part, but his performance on 25 October 1819

proved to be a triumph and even received a generous tribute from
Kean himself. Macready acted the part a number of times during
the season using the usual Colley Cibber version, but when he
played Gloucester in March 1821 he restored Shakespeare's text.
From then he remained at the head of his profession until he retired
in 1851.

He is depicted in the watercolour early in the play while still Duke
of Gloucester. It is signed and dated March 1820. It was not
engraved but was reproduced, from the collection of E Y Lowne in
Toynbee's edition of Macready's Diaries in 1912.

58 Daniel Terry (1780-1829) as Mr Simpson
Simpson and Co by John Poole
Drury Lane Theatre 1823
by **Samuel De Wilde**
watercolour   37.8 × 24.15 (14⅞ × 9½)

John Poole (1786-1872) wrote over thirty comedies and farces
between 1811 and 1836, after which he seems to have retired to
Paris, but died at the age of 87 in London, quite forgotten, though
he had added a name to the English language.

His play *Paul Pry* with Liston in the title role was produced at the
Haymarket Theatre in 1825 (see **73**). Among his other plays for
Liston were *Deaf as a Post* (1823) and *'Twould Puzzle a Conjurer*
(1824). *Simpson and Co* was first produced at Drury Lane Theatre
4 January 1823 with Daniel Terry in the role of Mr Simpson,
partner with Mr Bromley, in a firm of City merchants. It is a
comedy of matrimonial intrigue with Simpson as the eternal
innocent taking the blame for everybody else's faults, including his
partner's.

The moment depicted in the picture is in Act I.

Simpson (to his wife): "Don't throw cold water over me, my
darling; don't you see I'm gay, I'm joyous. On making up my
accounts of happiness, I find a large balance of content in my
favour, business goes on swimmingly; I've got a wife whom I love,
and, in short, all my little arrangements are mighty comfortable."

Daniel Terry, born in Bath, was originally articled to Wyatt, the
architect, but he had dabbled in amateur theatricals from his youth
and, finding no outlet for his architectural abilities, joined the
Sheffield Company as walking gentleman but rejoined Wyatt in
1803. He decided 'It is better to starve in a profession I do like, than
to suffer in one that I do not.' So he closed his compasses, and went
upon the stage.

He eventually reached London, from the provinces, in 1812 as
Lord Ogleby in *The Clandestine Marriage* at the Haymarket
Theatre and remained before the public until he died. *Oxberry's
Dramatic Biography* says: 'As an actor Mr Terry is the least
versatile upon the stage. It is not versatility to have your name put
in the bills for Dr Pangloss and King Lear and Sir Edward
Mortimer and Simpson. He plays them all in much the same style;
and seriously do we say it, when we speak of his comic old men we
always include his Lear.' The writer adds: 'Mr Terry can act
Simpson and it has no parallel on the stage. It is chaste, humorous,
natural, almost pathetic, for he blends perplexity with pathos: and
when fairly tired of laughing, you begin to pity him.'

Nevertheless he was also responsible for the adaptation of several
of Sir Walter Scott's novels for the stage – no mean task – which
include *Guy Mannering* (1816), *The Heart-of-Midlothian* (1819),
and *The Antiquary* (1820) (see **59**).

The De Wilde watercolour is not signed or dated; it was not
engraved. The watermark of the paper is 1822 and an old identification, originally on the mount, named Terry as the actor and the
play as *Simpson and Co*.

56

58

57 in colour on page *27*

59 William Blanchard (1769-1835) as Caxon
The Antiquary by Daniel Terry
(founded on the novel by Sir Walter Scott)
Covent Garden Theatre 1823
by **Samuel De Wilde**
watercolour   37.8 × 23.65 (14⅞ × 9⁵⁄₁₆)

Daniel Terry, actor and playwright, (see **58**) based his version of
Scott's *The Antiquary* on a previous play by Isaac Pocock which
failed at Covent Garden Theatre in 1820. Terry's adaptation was in
the form of a musical play, with music by Sir Henry Bishop and
Thomas Cooke (see **54**).

Bishop (1786-1855) was a noted English composer and conductor, a
prolific writer of some 130 ballad operas, musical pieces, ballads,
etc. He is remembered today for 'Home Sweet Home', written for
his opera *Clari, the Maid of Milan* (1823) and 'Lo, hear the gentle
lark', a coloratura soprano 'show piece'. He was knighted in 1842.

The Antiquary, founded on Scott's novel, published in 1816, tells
the story of a young officer, known as Major Neville, on whose
birth there is supposed to be a stain of illegitimacy. He falls in love
in England with Isabella Wardour, who, in deference to the
prejudices of her father, Sir Arthur Wardour, repulses him. Under
the assumed name of Lovel, he follows her to Scotland, falling in on
the way with Jonathan Oldbuck, laird of Monkbarns, a learned and
garrulous antiquary, and a neighbour of Sir Arthur. Lovel saves the
lives of Sir Arthur and his daughter at the peril of his own, fights a
duel with Hector McIntyre, Oldbuck's impetuous nephew, and
saves Sir Arthur from the ruin that his credulity and the impositions
of the German charlatan Dousterswivel have brought on him. He
finally turns out to be the son and heir of the Earl of Glenallan, and
all ends happily. Caxon is the servant to Jonathan Oldbuck and a
subsidiary character. William Blanchard created the part when the
musical piece was first produced at Covent Garden Theatre on
25 January 1820.

Blanchard, trained as a printer, joined a troupe of players at Buxton
in 1785, working his way up to management, but with little success.
He then joined the Norwich circuit before he made his London
debut at Covent Garden Theatre in October 1800. He remained
with the company for 34 years, specialising in old men, in the style
of Dowton, Farren and Fawcett, and was popular up to his retirement in 1835. He died shortly afterwards.

In the first scene of *The Antiquary* Caxon is waiting on the guests at
a picnic. Though now a servant he has formerly been a barber and
complains:

Caxon: "Ah me! hard times these for a poor barber! Time was when
the town of Fairport had as many wigs to dress and pigtails to tie, as
would keep me and a man at work every day, and all day long – and
now there's nothing to be seen but natural crops and bald heads:
there's no taste left now."

This is the moment in the watercolour, which is signed and dated
December 1823.

Blanchard played the part twice in 1823 in revivals of the piece on
23 and 31 May. A contemporary critic remarked that 'Blanchard
makes Caxon almost too much of a simpleton'.

60 William Farren (1786-1861) as Sir Peter Teazle
The School for Scandal by Richard Brinsley Sheridan
Covent Garden Theatre 1824/25
by **Samuel De Wilde**
watercolour   38 × 23.85 (14¹⁵⁄₁₆ × 9⅜)

Richard Brinsley Sheridan (1751-1816) combined three careers, as
a dramatist, theatre manager and politician. Three of his plays
remain masterpieces of the English 'Comedy of Manners'. *The
Rivals* (1775), *The School for Scandal* (1777), and *The Critic*
(1779). He also wrote musical pieces including *The Duenna* (1775)
and a pantomime *Robinson Crusoe* (1781) among others, as well as
the adaptation of other works. He bought Garrick's half share of
Drury Lane Theatre in 1776, became its manager and was
responsible for the rebuilding of the theatre in 1794. After the fire
of 1809 he was forced to cease its management. He had become a
Member of Parliament in 1780 and the money problems of his
multiple careers caused his breakdown and death in 1816. He was
buried in Westminster Abbey.

The School for Scandal was produced at Drury Lane Theatre on 8
May 1777 with Thomas King as Sir Peter. The play tells of the
trials of an elderly bachelor who has married a young wife from the
country who aspires to become a lady of fashion with all its
associated intrigues and foibles, much to the discomfiture of her
husband. William Farren (see **34, 56, 62**) played Sir Peter Teazle
at his London debut at Covent Garden Theatre on 10 September
1818 and it remained, with Lord Ogleby, one of his most famous
parts up to his retirement in 1851.

An old note on the mount (now destroyed) identifies the De Wilde
watercolour as of Farren as Sir Peter, but it is neither signed nor
dated. The paper is watermarked 1824 and it would seem likely that
it was painted during the 1824/5 Covent Garden season when
Farren was playing Sir Peter. There is no engraving after De Wilde
of him in this part.

Confusion has arisen as number **62** in this collection has for many
years been titled in both sale catalogues and exhibitions as Farren as
Sir Peter, which it is not.

59

60

61 Alexander Pope (1763-1835) as Dumont
The Tragedy of Jane Shore by Nicholas Rowe
Drury Lane Theatre 1824-5
by **Samuel De Wilde**
watercolour   37.5 × 23.3 (14¾ × 9⅛)

Nicholas Rowe (1674-1718) trained as a barrister and was called to the Bar but never practised. Instead he became a poet and dramatist on the fortune left by his father. His plays, mainly blank verse tragedies in the Elizabethan and Restoration manner, were popular in their day. They include *The Ambitious Step-Mother* (1700), *Tamerlane* (1701), *The Fair Penitent* (1703) and *The Tragedy of Jane Shore* (1714), his most famous play, which held the stage well into the nineteenth century. He is mainly remembered as the first 'modern' editor of Shakespeare, with the illustrated edition of the plays in 1709. He became Poet Laureate in 1714, but died soon afterwards, and was buried in Westminster Abbey.

Jane Shore, first produced at Drury Lane in 1714, is in a Shake-spearean mould, and tells of the final days of the former mistress of Edward IV: she is denounced to the Duke of Gloucester (soon to be Richard III) by Lady Alicia, who is jealous of the attentions that her lover Lord Hastings has showered on Jane. Having rebuffed Hastings, Jane now refuses to use her influence to persuade him to support Gloucester in his attempt to gain the throne, and the two are punished. Hastings is ordered to be killed, and Jane is condemned to do public penance; should anyone offer her food or shelter, he too shall be killed. Finally her husband, who has been in her service disguised as Dumont, comes to her aid. He is arrested, but not before he has forgiven his wife as she dies, repentant, in his arms.

Alexander Pope was born in Cork, into a family of architects. He went to art school in Dublin, and exhibited there up to 1780, when he returned to Cork, achieving great success in amateur dramatics. He became a professional there, making his debut in October 1781. He abandoned his artistic work and came to London, making his first appearance at Covent Garden Theatre in the title role of *Oronoko*, 8 January 1785. He then managed to combine his long acting career with that of an artist, exhibiting at the Royal Academy up to 1831, and had many theatrical sitters. He was married three times: firstly to Elizabeth Young, a successful leading lady, who died in 1797 and was buried in Westminster Abbey. His second wife was also an actress Maria Campion (Mrs Spencer) who followed her predecessor to the Abbey in 1803. In 1807, Pope married the widow of Francis Wheatley RA, who survived him.

Although he was not acclaimed by the critics, he was popular with the public, and his reputation as an actor was equalled by that as a gourmet: theatrical reminiscences abound with anecdotes of his culinary prowess.

The watercolour is signed and dated 'Jan (Mar?) 1825', and identi-fied as Alexander Pope both on the watercolour itself, and in a pencil note on the reverse: 'Alexander Pope, most likely as Dumont – *Jane Shore*'.

He played this part at Drury Lane in performances of the play between 1785 and his retirement in 1825. The costume strongly resembles the contemporary illustrations of the part in Act V, when Dumont reveals himself to his wife before she dies.

62 William Farren (1786-1861) as Sir Fretful Plagiary
The Critic by Richard Brinsley Sheridan
Covent Garden Theatre 1826
by **Samuel De Wilde**
watercolour   38.3 × 23.2 (15¹⁄₁₆ × 9⅛)

Sheridan's burlesque, *The Critic, or A Tragedy Rehearsed,* was first produced at Drury Lane Theatre 29 October 1779 with William Parsons as Sir Fretful. It is in the style of Buckingham's *The Rehearsal* (1671), satirising the pretentious playwrights and critics of the day and foibles of the actors. Sir Fretful (founded it is said on Cumberland) a petulant and conceited author, is invited, with other friends Dangle and Sneer, to watch a rehearsal of a play by a fellow dramatist, Mr Puff, with uproarious results.

The part of Sir Fretful was a great favourite of Charles Mathews. He was painted in the play by De Wilde both in oil and watercolour (Garrick Club collection); these and engravings of Farren and Terry (after Wageman circa 1819) as Sir Fretful all show the actors in a similar costume to that in the Maugham watercolour which has, for many years, been exhibited and catalogued as Farren as Sir Peter Teazle in *The School for Scandal* (see **60**).

The De Wilde watercolour is signed and dated April 1826 and shows Sir Fretful in the first act of the play when he comes to Dangle's house and finds him and his wife discussing the new play with Sneer. It has not been engraved. Farren first played the part in November 1818 at Covent Garden Theatre and it remained one of his parts throughout his long career.

63 Charles Mayne Young (1777-1856) as Pierre
Venice Preserv'd, or A Plot Discovered by Thomas Otway
Covent Garden Theatre 1826
by **Samuel De Wilde**
watercolour   38.1 × 24 (15 × 9⁷⁄₁₆)

Otway's play *Venice Preserv'd, or A Plot Discovered* (see **3**) remained in the repertoire for many years, offering a challenge to two leading actors in the roles of Pierre and Jaffier.

The moment depicted in the painting is when Pierre is brought before the Senate to be condemned to death.

Pierre: "Why these disgraceful chains upon the limbs
    That have so often labour'd in your service?
    Are these the wreaths of triumphs ye bestow
    On those that bring you Conquests home and Honours?"

Charles Mayne Young was a follower of the Kemble school of acting and made his debut in Liverpool in 1798. He came to London in 1807 playing Hamlet at the Haymarket Theatre. He remained a reliable actor for many years supporting his greater contemporaries, though at times he played leading roles he created few parts of importance. He retired in 1832.

Young played Pierre to the Jaffier of Charles Kemble at Covent Garden Theatre 29 September 1826. The watercolour is signed and dated 182(6?). The paper is watermarked 1825.

64 Unidentified actor
in an unidentified play 1827/8
by **Samuel De Wilde**
watercolour   37.65 × 21.5 (14¹³⁄₁₆ × 9½)

The watercolour is signed and dated 182(8?). The paper is water-marked 1827.

The actor resembles Charles Taylor (1781-1847) (see **50**). There are two engravings of him (after De Wilde), in ballad operas (*The Quaker* and *Inkle and Yarico*, in both of which he played in 1803) which are similar in likeness and costume; but there is no trace of him acting in metropolitan theatres at the date of the watercolour. Therefore the identification of this picture must be left for further research.

61

62

63

64

65

65 **Charles Mathews** (1776-1835) as Mathew Stuffy
The Actor of All Work by George Colman the Younger
Haymarket Theatre 1817
by **William De Lamotte**
watercolour   27.9 × 17 (11 × 6¹¹/₁₆)

66 **Charles Mathews** as a French Tragedian
watercolour   27.3 × 19.4 (10¾ × 7⅝)

67 **Charles Mathews** as Andrew MacSillergrip
watercolour   27.9 × 17 (11 × 6¹¹/₁₆)

68 **Charles Mathews** as Mrs MacSillergrip
watercolour   26.8 × 15.1 (10⁹/₁₆ × 5¹⁵/₁₆)

69 **Charles Mathews** as a Fat Coachman
watercolour   27.9 × 17.8 (11 × 7)

The Actor of All Work, or First and Second Floor was adapted by
Colman from a French farce as a vehicle for Mathews who played,
as Multiple, a strolling actor, six characters. With the assistance of
Conner as the Manager of a Country Theatre, Miss Carr as a Little
Boy, Multiple's Manservant, and a double set, it was first produced
at the Haymarket Theatre 13 August 1815. The plot is slight.
Multiple has been refused an engagement by Velinspeck, a country
manager, on the grounds of his incapability, so – as they happen to
be occupying two rooms in the same house, on the first and second
floors – the actor sets out to convince the manager, by appearing
before him in various characters, of his ability. Firstly as a
prompter, Mathew Stuffy, then as a French Tragedian (an
impersonation of Talma), followed by Robin Scrawky, an
Apprentice, Andrew MacSillergrip, a Scotch Pawnbroker, Mrs
MacSillergrip, his wife, and finally a Fat Coachman. By this device
he convinces the manager of his talents, and is engaged.

Five of the six characters in the play are depicted in this series of
watercolours which are signed, dated and inscribed by De Lamotte.
It was the success of this farce that led Mathews to begin his
'Entertainments' the following year. He developed a form of
one-man performance called an 'At Home'. In these he introduced
many characters – by means of quick changes, ventriloquism and
trick settings. He gave these with varying titles, at both the Lyceum
and Adelphi theatres as well as all over the provinces and in
America, while continuing to appear as an actor in plays.

66

67

68

69

70 Thomas Potter Cooke (1786-1864) as Roderick Dhu
The Lady of the Lake by Thomas Dibdin
(founded on the poem by Sir Walter Scott)
Surrey Theatre 1818
by **John Boaden**
oil 70 × 52 (27½ × 20½)

Thomas Dibdin (1771-1841), illegitimate son of Charles Dibdin, the actor, writer and composer, followed in his father's footsteps as actor and writer. He was stage manager at Sadler's Wells, and later manager of the Surrey Theatre, which his father had built as the Royal Circus in 1782. In 1810 Elliston renamed it the Surrey Theatre, and it was here under his management on 4 September 1810 that Dibdin's own adaptation of Sir Walter Scott's poem *The Lady of the Lake* was produced, with T P Cooke as Roderick. The play was revived for one night under Dibdin's own management at the Surrey on 26 October 1818, Cooke again played the part of Roderick. It was at this time that the painting by John Boaden was executed.

The moment depicted is when Roderick (the rebel chieftain) and Fitzjames (the king in disguise) meet at daybreak, amid 'A picturesque assemblage of Craggy Rocks.' The two men confront each other. Fitzjames says his one wish is to meet Roderick in mortal combat. "Have then thy wish! thy rashness rue," retorts Roderick. He blows a whistle and, after 'Short Music' – 'Enter the whole Band of Highlanders among the Rocks, so as completely to fill every part.'

> "These are Clan Alpine's warriors true –
> And, Saxon, I am Roderick Dhu!"

T P Cooke, the son of a surgeon, was born in 1786. He became a sailor in 1796 but left the sea for the stage. His first London appearance was in 1804. He established himself as a leading actor when he played Ruthven in *The Vampire* at the Lyceum in 1820, but it was as William in *Black Ey'd Susan*, which he first played at the Surrey in 1829, that he is best remembered. In 1853, when he was starting an engagement at the Standard Theatre, Shoreditch, he was said to have played Roderick Dhu 250 times and William 785.

The painting is signed and dated 1819 and was engraved by Charles Picart the same year for *The Theatrical Inquisitor*.

71 Edmund Kean (1787-1833) as Gloucester
Richard III by William Shakespeare
Drury Lane 1819
after **George Clint,** by an unknown artist
oil 39 × 29 (15½ × 11½)

This painting shows the moment in Act I, Scene 2 of the Colley Cibber version, when Gloucester woos the Lady Anne.

Gloucester: "Take up the sword again, or take up me".

It is a copy of an original by George Clint. There are traces of a signature and date on the hat but they are indecipherable. The date appears to be 182–, the last numeral is either a 3 or a 5, which makes it definitely a copy as it was first engraved in 1822 by R Cooper. Also all the Clint paintings recorded are unsigned and of a superior quality to this picture. It is probable that the original was painted in either 1819 or 20 when Kean was sitting to Clint for another picture.

There are two studies for the original in existence, one in the Garrick Club (wrongly catalogued as Sir Giles Overreach) and the other, which belonged to Irving, is now in the Museum of the City of New York. The whereabouts of the finished painting is not recorded and has so far remained untraced.

Edmund Kean appeared at Drury Lane on 26 January 1814 as Shylock, and on 12 February played Gloucester and became established as the greatest actor of the contemporary English stage. His story is too well known for repetition here, but it is worth noting that he went to America for the first time in 1820, just after the period of the painting. He played in *Richard III* at the Haymarket on 16 September 1820, and did not return to London till 1821, when he reappeared at Drury Lane on 23 July – again as Gloucester.

72 Robert William Elliston (1774-1831) as Ranger
The Suspicious Husband by Dr Benjamin Hoadley
Drury Lane 1823
by **E F Lambert**
watercolour 27.9 × 18.6 (11 × 7⁵⁄₁₆)

The Suspicious Husband, a comedy by Dr Benjamin Hoadley (1705-1757), was first produced at Covent Garden Theatre in 1747 with Garrick as Ranger, and was highly successful. 'Its merits', it is recorded 'are, perhaps, pleasing rather than striking, and the vivacity of the plot and action prevents its imperfections of design, character and language, from being too rigidly noticed, yet the parts of Ranger, Mr Strictland, and Clarinda, are lively, well-drawn, and expressive. The former is a perfect portrait of a thoughtless, spirited, and undesigning rover, from whom it was originally intended to have called this piece *The Rake* and to Garrick's inimitable performance of the part may be chiefly attributed to the success of the Comedy during its first run.'

Ranger was also one of Elliston's successes, a part he first played in 1819. Elliston, self-styled 'The Great Lessee' was intended for the Church but left home to become an actor in 1791. He made his London debut at the Haymarket Theatre in 1796 and became extremely popular. He was an eccentric character with a passion for management and either took over, or opened, many provincial playhouses. In London he became lessee of the Surrey Theatre in 1809, the Olympic Theatre in 1813, and Drury Lane from 1819 to 1826 when he became bankrupt. He returned to the Surrey where he made his final appearance in 1831.

The watercolour is signed and dated 1823, it was not engraved. Elliston played the part of Ranger in a revival at Drury Lane in 1822 and again in October 1823. There is also an engraving (after Wageman) of him in the part published in the magazine *The Drama,* April 1823.

72

70

71

73 John Liston (1776-1846) as Apollo Belvi
Killing No Murder by Theodore Hook
Drury Lane Theatre 1823
by E F Lambert
watercolour   17.95 × 21.25 (11 × 8⅜)

Theodore Hook's musical farce *Killing No Murder* was first produced at the Haymarket Theatre on 21 August 1809 (see **43**) with Charles Mathews as Buskin and John Liston as Apollo Belvi.

In an amusing preface to *Killing No Murder* Hook tells of his difficulties with the censor, a Methodist, who objected to what he considered an unnecessary attack made upon this sect in the play. In consequence of this, one scene (relating Apollo Belvi's adventures as a Methodist preacher) and various allusions had to be deleted before the play was granted a licence in 1809.

Belvi, now a dancing master, has told his adventures to Buskin and at the end of the scene (in Act II) they conclude with a song and dance in which Belvi sings:

> "Mark the entrechat de six,
> With the twirling of the body."

(See also **75** for the portrait of Webster in the same part and at the same moment).

Liston first appeared in the provinces before he made his London debut at the Haymarket in 1805. He remained associated with that theatre for many years where he created some of the most famous characters, Sam Swipes (1820), Van Dunder (1824), and Paul Pry (1825). He became the highest-paid comedian of his day and the most publicised. His face and figure were to be seen on prints, in china, as jugs and on snuff boxes. The name 'Paul Pry' in John Poole's play passed into the language to describe 'one of those idle, meddling fellows, who, having no employment of their own, are perpetually interfering in the affairs of other people.' His catch phrases became part of conversation. 'I hope I don't intrude' – 'Just dropped in' and 'It's nothing to me.'

Liston appeared at Covent Garden and Drury Lane in his big successes. He first played Apollo Belvi at the Lane in a revival of the play on 5 February 1823 at which time the watercolour, signed and dated 1823, was executed. It was lithographed in colour by W Sheldricks the same year.

74 Frederick Henry Yates (1797-1842) as an old lady
in one of his 'Entertainments'
Adelphi Theatre 1827-29
by Thomas Wageman?
watercolour   22.5 × 19.2 (9⁵⁄₁₆ × 7⁹⁄₁₉)

Yates, a popular comedian, began his solo 'Entertainments', in the style of Charles Mathews, at the Adelphi Theatre in 1826. He later developed a 'double' programme with William Blanchard, and in 1829 was joined by Mathews himself.

Yates included many female characters in these programmes including 'Paulina Pry', wife of Paul Pry, who had 'Just drop't in, in her husband's absence!', and later 'she' became Paul's mother. In 1827, in what was billed as a Monopologue called *Stop Thief!*, he played all the parts, which included Emily Simpson (a Young Lady), Penelope Pops (a Maiden Lady), and Mrs M'Nigglewick (a Lady in search of her Fourth Husband).

The watercolour is unsigned and is definitely of Yates, but cannot be pinned down to any particular character. The attribution to an artist is debatable. De Wilde was at one time suggested, but he last exhibited in 1821. It is felt that Wageman is a strong possibility. The picture dates from after 1826 (the date of the watermark of the paper on which it is drawn).

75 Benjamin Webster (1797-1882) as Apollo Belvi
in *Killing No Murder* by Theodore Hook
Haymarket Theatre 1831
by Robert William Buss
oil   54.5 × 42 (21½ × 16½)

Theodore Hook's musical farce (see **43**) was first produced at the Haymarket Theatre in 1809 with Liston in the part of Belvi (see **73**).

The play was revived at the Haymarket Theatre, with Benjamin Webster as Belvi, on 16 June 1831. He was the founder of the famous stage family, firstly a child dancer in the provinces, and later in London. He became an actor with Madame Vestris at the Olympic, and in 1837 took the Haymarket, which he managed for sixteen years. He was also manager of the Adelphi from 1844 to his retirement in 1874. During this time he engaged the best actors and writers of his day and founded the tradition of Adelphi Drama, which persisted until the end of the century. As an actor he was unsurpassed in his day in character parts.

The painting depicts Belvi at the same moment as in **73**.

The picture was engraved by H Robertson as the frontispiece to the play in Cumberland's *Minor Theatre*, 1833.

76 John Baldwin Buckstone (1802-1879) as Spado
The Castle of Andalusia by John O'Keeffe
Haymarket Theatre 1833
by Robert William Buss
oil   54.5 × 42 (21½ × 16½)

O'Keeffe and Arnold's comic opera, first produced in 1782, was often revived (see **18** and **51**). It was given at the Haymarket Theatre on 16 July 1833 with Webster in the part of Spado (created by John Quick).

In the highly-involved plot, Spado, a member of a troupe of bandits, is a small, cowardly rogue. He is a buffoon and their butt though he has a cunning brain and is not above betraying them for his own ends. He gives information to the owner of the castle, only to discover he has been overheard. His quick wit and inventive brain come to his rescue. He pretends that all he has just told only occurred in a dream.

This is the moment depicted in the picture (Act II, Scene 1).

Don Scipio: (owner of the castle) "What the devil then, is this all but a dream you have been telling me?"
Spado: "Ay, sir, and the most frightful dream I ever had in my life. I'm at this instant frightened out of my wits."

J B Buckstone was articled to a solicitor, but gave up the law for the stage, and after a successful apprenticeship in the provinces first appeared in London at the Surrey Theatre in 1823. In 1827 he was at the Adelphi in his own play, *Luke the Labourer*, and from 1833 to 1839 was in the summer seasons at the Haymarket Theatre. He was in America from 1840 to 1842, and on his return reopened the Haymarket, of which theatre he eventually became manager from 1853 till his death in 1879.

Buckstone wrote both plays for his theatre and acted in them, surrounding himself with a talented company, making his regime one of the most memorable in the history of the theatre. He was an excellent droll comedian, and to this day his ghost is reputed to haunt the Haymarket Theatre: the manifestation is said to presage a highly-successful production.

The painting as Spado is signed with a monogram and dated 1833, and was engraved by Hollis as the frontispiece to the play in Cumberland's *British Theatre*, 1834.

75

74

76

73

77 William Pleater Davidge (1814-1888) as Malvolio
Twelfth Night, or What You Will by William Shakespeare
painted c 1846 by **Henry Andrews,**
oil   62 × 50 (24½ × 19¾)

William Davidge was born in London and was an enthusiastic
amateur actor as a boy. His first appearance on the professional
stage was at Nottingham in June 1836. He appeared in London at
the Queen's Theatre, Tottenham Street on 26 September of the
same year. He followed this with appearances at the minor theatres
of London, including the Royal Victoria; but it was in the provinces
that he became a successful leading man. He was engaged at the
Theatre Royal, Manchester, for the 1843-44 season and remained
there till 1846. It was during this period that he played Malvolio on
13 February 1846 – one of his biggest successes: 'His air of
inordinate conceit and self-satisfaction is irresistibly ludicrous, and
of the whole performance, from the finding of the letter and
assumption of the cross-garters to the final exit and assurance of
revenge, evinces real genius. Mr Davidge has repeatedly played the
part at the Theatre Royal, Manchester, and so successfully as to
render *Twelfth Night* a stock piece on their boards.' He also played
the part in various provincial towns before going to America in 1850
where he died in 1888.

There is no trace of him playing Malvolio in London after his
success in the part at Manchester, and it is most likely that the
painting was executed there in 1846.

Malvolio is depicted soliloquising as to how he would bear himself
should he become master of the house, just before he notices the
letter, placed in his way by Maria.

There are traces of a signature and a date on the painting but they
are indecipherable. When it passed through Christies in 1919 it was
said to be by Henry Andrews and of Davidge. There is no reason to
doubt this attribution.

78 Unidentified actor as Macall
& in an unidentified play
79 by an unknown artist, signed 'D. Wilde' mid-1820s
pencil and wash sketches 36.7 × 23.2 (14¾ × 9¼)

These two pencil sketches with a watercolour wash, on paper
watermarked 1825, would appear to be from a sketchbook or pad
(other roughs are on the reverse). They are of the same actor in the
same costume, and, though having a contemporary inscription and a
signature 'D. Wilde', are obviously not by Samuel De Wilde. The
pencil inscriptions are on **78**: "Mac. Hurry up Jack Marrall Scene
2nd Act 4th", and on **79**: "Macall. I! No, I assure you! I have no
conscience etc. Act 5th Scene 1".

80 Unidentified actor
in an unidentified play
by an unknown artist signed 'D. Wilde' mid-1820s
watercolour   21.4 × 15.2 (8⁷⁄₁₆ × 6)

The signature is similar to **78** and **79** and an equally poor piece of
work. The character looks like Sir Anthony Absolute in *The Rivals*
but could equally be Sir Peter Teazle or any other angry gentleman
in 'old comedy' and a very poor likeness of William Farren.

78, 79 and **80** are undoubtedly not the work of Samuel De Wilde.

81 A Gentleman (Captain Wilts?)
in Masquerade costume: 'The Times' 1769
by Johan Zoffany?
oil   86 × 70 (34 × 27½)

This painting is first recorded in 1926 with the title 'Portrait of
Horne Tooke' by Zoffany. Tooke was a parson-politician and
supporter of John Wilkes, not an actor. Later, in the Maugham
collection in 1948, the painting was said to be 'Samuel Foote
delivering a prologue or epilogue to an unknown play at the
Haymarket', a description afterwards modified to 'An unknown
actor by Zoffany'.

While investigating this picture, attention was drawn to an engraving titled: ' 'The Times', taken from an Original Character which
appear'd at the Masquerade at Lincoln, Dec 21st, 1769'. This is the
exact costume as in the painting (fully described with an explanation of the political allusions in *The Artist and the Theatre*). The
engraving is undated but an advertisement in *The Public Advertiser*,
27 January 1770, records: 'On Monday will be published, Price 1s.,
a New Print of *The Times*, being the real masquerade character in
which Capt. W—s appeared at Lincoln, Dec 21st, 1769 – truly
Satyric, Characteristic and Burlesque . . .' There is an allusion to
this print in 'Particulars of the Soho Masquerade, Carlisle House'
(Mrs Cornelys) in *The Town and Country Magazine*, May 1770. A
description of characters at masquerade includes: 'Mr Wilts
supported the character of *The Times* as represented on a new
Print'.

The costume depicted in the print has two references to Lincoln
which are not in the painting. Before the recent cleaning of the
picture it appeared that also the band round the loins of the sitter
marked 'standing forces', a political *double entendre*, had also been
omitted, but this is now faintly visible and appears to have been
painted out at some time, probably in respect to Victorian modesty!

It would seem that the Capt. W—s who wore the costume at
Lincoln (shown in the print), and the 'Mr Wilts' who wore a similar
costume to Mrs Cornelys' Soho masquerade, are the same
gentleman and that he had his portrait painted in London (the local
references to Lincoln being omitted).

It has not been possible to trace any reference to a Captain (or Mr)
Wilts, or find a portrait of him for comparison; therefore some
element of doubt about the identity of the sitter remains, though
the subject has been definitely identified as a masquerade costume –
thus making the picture unfortunately non-theatrical in its origin.
The attribution to Zoffany remains to be established but, as with **16**
and **80,** Thomas Parkinson is a possibility.

77

80

78

79

81

82

83

82 Taste
from a set of paintings representing 'The Five Senses'
painted 1791
by **Jan Ekels the Younger**
oil   65 × 60 (25½ × 23½)

The early history of this painting has not been traced. It was in 1947 titled as a 'Scene from a play by Samuel De Wilde' and, as this, was acquired by Maugham.

Research into possible plays and actors c 1795 (of the period of the picture) led nowhere. It was also felt that it was not by De Wilde. Information from museum experts on the furniture, glasses, etc. in the painting, led to the conclusion that the painting was of Dutch origin.

The Director of the Department of Paintings of the Rijksmuseum, Amsterdam, and Dr Gerson of the Rijksbureau voor Kunsthistorische Documentatie at The Hague, both recognised the painting as the work of Jan Ekels the Younger, of Amsterdam, and related to other known pictures by the artist showing the five senses.

Another version of *Taste*, signed and dated 1791, was sold at Christie's in 1964, with a pair of *Hearing (Sound)*; and a third, signed and dated 1791, is in the Stedelikjk Museum, 'De Lakenhal' in Leiden. Although the composition varies, the 'models' are the same. Further research also brought to light two paintings in Germany titled *Sound* and *Smell*, belonging to a set of paintings of 'The Five Senses', which were also signed and dated 1791. The Maugham picture is not signed or dated, but there is no doubt that it is related to such a series.

83 Unknown subject
by an unknown artist
oil   56 × 39 (22 × 15¼)

This picture has had several identifications attached to it. On the back of the stretcher is written: 'Foote and Weston in Dr Last,' and is credited to Zoffany. It is first recorded in 1863 with this title and artist. But by 1937 the artist had been changed to Samuel De Wilde, and by the first exhibition of the Maugham Collection at the Victoria and Albert Museum it had become, for some unaccountable reason, 'A scene from *The School for Scandal* by De Wilde.' By costume, the subject dates from about 1770, too early for De Wilde, though Zoffany was in London until 1772 when he went to Florence until 1779. Once again Thomas Parkinson is a possibility.

Foote and Weston are depicted in the Zoffany/Finlayson painting (**9** in this collection) in *The Devil Upon Two Sticks* as the Devil and Dr Last. They also appeared together in a play by Bickerstaffe, *Dr Last and his Chariot*, at the Haymarket in 1769, when Foote played an imaginary invalid and Weston Dr Last: the play was not a success. The texts of both these plays have been examined and they do not have an incident to fit the picture, neither is there any similarity to these actors.

The subject represents a little man dressed completely in black, except for his white shirt-cuffs, expounding over the back of a chair to another man, who rests one knee on the chair; and is also dressed in black with a white shirt and stock, and has a powdered wig, while the little man appears to wear his own iron-grey hair. The tall man seems to be putting something in his mouth, or cracking a nut with his teeth.

It is very likely that it is a non-theatrical picture and possibly represents what would appear to be a legal disputation, probably an incident from fiction.

Notes on Artists
All references are to picture numbers, not page numbers

Andrews, Henry (18?-1868)
77

Henry Andrews exhibited at the Royal Academy from 1830 to 1838, and at the British Institution from 1831 to 1847 – mainly historical subjects. He painted a number of pictures in the style of Watteau. There is a painting by him of the trial scene from *Henry VIII* as it was played at Covent Garden in 1831 with Fanny Kemble, Charles Kemble, etc, in the Picture Gallery of the Royal Shakespeare Theatre, Stratford-upon-Avon. Andrews was also a lithographer, and there are several theatrical subjects in this medium; these include a portrait of Miss O'Bryan (Dancer), and a set of four portraits in character of Elizabeth Poole (Singer), c 1831. No further theatrical subjects have been traced.

Boaden, John (17?-1839)
70

Little is recorded about the life of John Boaden (son of James Boaden, pamphletist and biographer) but his output was prolific. Between 1810 and 1833 he exhibited some forty portraits at the Royal Academy, many of them theatrical. He exhibited ninety paintings at the British Institution (1810-1839) including portraits, fancy Shakespearean subjects, (probably for his father's book on Shakespeare, published in 1824) and landscapes.

Brown, Mather (c1763-1831)
11

Brown was born in New England and came to Britain in the wake of the American troubles. He became a pupil of Benjamin West in London and had a long and fairly successful career as an historical painter. He exhibited at the Royal Academy from 1782 to 1831, held several official positions, and contributed to the Boydell *Shakespeare Gallery*. He painted several large theatrical subjects and an album of his portrait drawings is in the National Portrait Gallery of Scotland. He was an assistant to Reynolds and was responsible for many copies and 'second versions' of his paintings. His painting of Joseph Holman and Anne Brunton as Romeo and Juliet is in the Mander and Mitchenson Collection.

Buss, Robert William (1804-1875)
75, 76

Robert William Buss, pupil of George Clint (whose son Alfred married Buss's sister) exhibited at the Royal Academy and elsewhere from 1826 to 1859, and at least fifteen of his theatrical paintings were engraved, mostly as illustrations to the plays in Cumberland's *British Theatre*. He is most remembered today as one of the first illustrators of Dickens's *Pickwick Papers*. When Robert Seymour ('Phiz') died, after only completing his drawing for the second number, Buss was hurriedly called in to supply the illustrations for the third part; but as he was inexperienced in etching – in which process the illustrations were to be executed – he did not continue with the work. His main canvases are historical and humorous subjects of the type admired by the mid-Victorians. His early theatrical subjects follow in the De Wilde tradition. The two pictures in the Maugham collection are among his early works for Cumberland. Another two are in the Mander and Mitchenson Collection. His sister, Frances Mary, was the famous pioneer of women's education.

Clint, George ARA (1770-1854)
71

Clint was born near Drury Lane, where his father was a hairdresser. On leaving school, he was apprenticed to a fishmonger, then bound to a lawyer. Disliking both occupations, and being left to fend for himself, he became a house painter. He later turned to painting as an art, and worked on sign boards and miniatures. His work was brought to the notice of Sir William Beechy, who encouraged him; he became an expert engraver in mezzotint, and his engraving of Harlow's painting of the Kemble family in the trial scene in *Henry VIII* brought him to the public notice and started him on a successful career as a portrait painter. His scenes from plays achieved great popularity (by their engravings) and he was elected ARA in 1821. As a theatrical artist, Clint stands in a line with Zoffany, De Wilde, and Buss.

Dance, Sir Nathaniel, RA (1734-1811)
12

Sir Nathaniel Dance was a pupil of Francis Hayman and achieved success as a portrait and historical painter. He was one of the Founder Members of the Royal Academy, from which he retired in 1790, when he married a wealthy widow, gave up painting, and entered politics. He was MP for East Grinstead from 1790 to 1802, and from 1807 till his death in 1811. He took the name of Holland and was created a baronet in 1800.

De Lamotte, William Alfred (1775-1863)
65-69

William De Lamotte was a landscape painter, watercolourist, and lithographer. He was drawing master at Sandhurst Military Academy. His main work is non-theatrical. His son, Philip, also a drawing master, was an important early photographer.

De Wilde, Samuel (c1751-1832)
21-64

De Wilde was the son of a Dutch immigrant woodcarver who came to England in the first half of the 18th century. It was in London, and not in Holland as has previously been thought, that Samuel De Wilde was born. For a time he was apprenticed to his father's trade. In 1769 he became a student at the newly-formed Royal Academy Schools. He is said to have first become known for etchings and mezzotints under the pseudonym 'Paul' but the reason for this attribution has yet to be shown. He exhibited under his own name at Spring Gardens from 1776 to 1778, and at the Royal Academy from 1778 to 1821.

His first theatrical subjects at the Royal Academy date from 1792, though some of his work, commissioned as illustrations to the plays in Bell's *British Theatre*, probably dates from 1790. Only one or two earlier theatrical portraits are known and his career as a theatrical portrait painter really begins with the *British Theatre*.

He is remembered for his fine series of oil portraits of actors and actresses in character, many of which were engraved. Edward Fitzgerald, in a letter to Fanny Kemble, said 'He (De Wilde) never missed likeness, character and life, even when reduced to a 16mo engraving.' He made countless watercolour portraits, now highly-prized as records of the stage during his period. His studio was conveniently placed between Drury Lane and Covent Garden, in Taverstock Row.

In his later years he was still often seen in Drury Lane, with his portfolio under his arm. He ceased to exhibit in 1821 but continued to produce competent work until at least 1827. He died in 1832, aged over eighty, and was interred in the burying ground of Whitefields Tabernacle, Tottenham Court Road.

Although most of his watercolours are dated, the actors are not identified by the artist. As so many are of lesser known actors or singers, often in subsidiary parts, it is sometimes difficult now to be precise, though luckily they are mostly of performances near the date of execution. His commissioned work, engraved for publication as frontispieces to plays, or as magazine illustrations, is an early form of personal publicity, for particular performers. He received comparatively small sums for his work: whole length drawings costing from £2.12s 6d, and oils up to 12 guineas are recorded in his 1810-11 diary.

The Maugham collection of paintings and drawings by De Wilde is second only in size and importance to that of the Garrick Club.

Ekels, Jan (the Younger) (1759-1793)
82
Born in Amsterdam, the son and pupil of Jan Ekels the Elder. After an early trip to Paris he remained in Amsterdam painting mostly genre scenes, but also landscapes and portraits, though he does not appear to have painted theatrical subjects.

Finlayson, John (1730-1776)
5, 9
Finlayson had a short career as a mezzotint engraver that probably lasted about eight years. He exhibited prints at the Society of Artists from 1768 to 1770, all of them theatrical. He engraved at least one work after his own design, and exhibited portraits and miniatures in 1762 and 1763.

Hamilton, William, RA (1751-1801)
13, 14
Hamilton was born of Scottish parents living in Chelsea. His father was an assistant of the Adam brothers, and Robert Adam paid for the boy to study with Zucchi in Italy. Hamilton first exhibited at the Royal Academy in 1769. From 1780 to 1789 he chiefly painted portraits, two of the best known being of Sarah Siddons – one in *Isabella* with her little son, and another in *The Grecian Daughter* – and a third of John Philip Kemble in *Richard III*, all of which have been engraved. The original of the latter is in the Mander and Mitchenson Collection. Hamilton was responsible for numerous paintings in the Boydell *Shakespeare Gallery*.

Hayman, Francis, RA (1708-1776)
2
Hayman was born in Exeter and was first employed as a scene painter at Drury Lane. He was well known as a decorative artist and painted a number of works for Jonathan Tyers at Vauxhall Gardens. With Gravelot, he designed the illustrations to Hamner's Shakespeare of 1744, introducing into English painting a light French style. He was President of the Society of Artists from 1766 to 1768 and a founder member of the Royal Academy.

Lambert, E F (exhibited 1823-1846)
72, 73
Lambert was a portrait and historical painter and engraver who exhibited in London at the Royal Academy and Suffolk Street from 1823-1846.

Parkinson, Thomas (1744-17?)
18, 81, 83
Parkinson was admitted as a student at the Royal Academy Schools in 1771, though he began exhibiting in 1769. He painted a number of theatrical subjects in the manner of Zoffany, and his work has often been mistaken for this artist. Parkinson also executed drawings for Bell's Shakespeare (c 1775). He exhibited at the Royal Academy up to 1789).

Reynolds, Sir Joshua, PRA (1723-1792)
11
Reynolds was born in Plympton and moved to London in 1740 for a four year apprenticeship to Thomas Hudson. He visited Italy from 1749 to 1753 and later used his knowledge of Roman High Renaissance painting to dominate English portrait painting with his 'Grand Style'. He became the most successful portrait painter of the eighteenth century in England, painter to the King, and first President of the Royal Academy. He saw himself as an History Painter and contributed to the Boydell *Shakespeare Gallery*. He was a close friend of Garrick and painted him several times.

Smirke, Robert, RA (1752-1845)
15
Born near Carlisle in 1752, Smirke was a student at the Royal Academy Schools. He was elected ARA in 1791 and RA in 1793. He painted many small pictures commissioned for engravings to illustrate plays, poems, and novels. Many of these he excuted in monochrome. He was also one of the artists employed by Boydell for his *Shakespeare Gallery*. He continued to paint till late in life, dying in his ninety-third year in 1845. Ten of his paintings – all illustrations to Shakespeare – are now in the Picture Gallery of the Royal Shakespeare Theatre, Stratford-upon-Avon.

Stothard, Thomas, RA (1755-1834)
20
Stothard was born in Long Acre, London in 1755, and was bound apprentice to a pattern-drawer in Spitalfields; but his ability for design gained him commissions to illustrate magazines, and for some years he worked for leading publishers. He later began to paint in oils and was elected to the Royal Academy in 1794; he became its librarian in 1813.
Though less successful as a painter, he is best remembered as an illustrator, and no less than three thousand of his designs were engraved, covering a wide field of literature, poetry, and plays.

Van Loo, Jean-Baptiste (1684-1745)
1
Van Loo was of Flemish origin, born in France. He achieved great popularity as a portrait painter, first in Italy and later in France. During his stay in London, from 1737 to 1742, he painted many portraits of the nobility and the fashionable world. His sitters included Colley Cibber and Peg Woffington.

Wageman, Thomas Charles (1787-1863)
74
Wageman was portrait painter to the King of Holland and exhibited at the Royal Academy from 1813 to 1848. His small portraits in pencil or watercolour are mainly theatrical and many of them were engraved as frontispieces for theatrical journals and plays. He was also an engraver and worked often from De Wilde originals.

Zoffany, Johan, RA (1733-1810)
3, 4, 5, 6, 7, 8, 9, 10, 81
Johan Zoffany (Johan Zauffely) was born at Ratisbon in Germany; his father, of Bohemian descent, was architect to the Prinz von Thurn und Taxis. Young Zoffany ran away to Rome at the age of thirteen to study painting. After twelve years he returned to Germany and made an unhappy marriage, which led him to come to England in 1758.

At first he was extremely poor, so became an assistant to Benjamin Wilson, and through him met David Garrick, whom he had first painted about 1762. He had by then become a member of the Society of Artists, and his successful portrait of the Earl of Barrymore caused Lord Bute to recommend him to the Royal Family. He quickly became famous as a painter of society and theatrical portraits and was elected to the Royal Academy in 1769. In 1772 he left England for Italy, returning in 1779, and between 1784 and 1790 made a voyage to India. His last years were spent at Strand-on-the-Green, and he is buried in Kew churchyard.

His theatrical pictures were exhibited at the Society of Artists and at the Royal Academy between 1762 and 1796.

Index of Plays All references are to picture numbers, not page numbers

Index of Actors

All references are to picture numbers, not page numbers

Photograph acknowledgements

All colour photography by Prudence Cuming Associates.

Black and white photographs as follows:

Photograph of W Somerset Maugham by Camera Press.

1, 2, 5, 7, 9, 10, 12, 14, 18, 19, 22, 23, 27, 31, 32, 33, 35, 70, 71, 74, 75, 76, 77, 81, 82, by The Victoria and Albert Museum;

3, 4, 6, 8, 11, 13, 15, 16, 20, 21, 24, 25, 26, 28, 29, 30, 34, 41, 42, 43, 46, 48, 51, 53, 56, 57 by Prudence Cuming Associates;

17, 36, 37, 38, 39, 40, 44, 45, 47, 49, 50, 52, 54, 55, 58, 59, 60, 61, 62, 63, 64, 65, 66, 67, 68, 69, 72, 78, 79, 80 by David Hughes;